The Art of Making Sex Sacred

TECHNIQUES FOR INTIMATE RELATIONSHIPS

By
Guru Terath Kaur Khalsa, Ph.D.

Based on the Teachings of
Master of Kundalini Yoga
Yogi Bhajan, Ph.D.

YOGI JI PRESS

Published and Distributed by:
Yogi Ji Press
P.O. Box 970 Santa Cruz, NM 87567
Tel: (505) 753-5086
Fax: (505)753-9249
E-mail: nam @ newmexico. com
Write for catalog and to be on our mailing list

Publisher – Parmatma Singh Khalsa
Editors – Parmatma Singh Khalsa and Sarb Nam Kaur Khalsa
Editorial Assistant – Narayan Kaur Khalsa
Book Design – Pritpal Singh Khalsa
Cover Design – Pritpal Singh Khalsa
Cover Illustration – Hari Jiwan Kaur Khalsa
Other Illustrations:
    Yoga Postures and Venus Kriyas – Simrat Kaur Khalsa
    Moon Centers – Hari Jiwan Kaur Khalsa
    Chakras – Hari Jiwan Kaur Khalsa

 KRI Seal of Approval

Disclaimer

Before we begin...

    This book is based upon the centuries-old yogic tradition of Kundalini Yoga. The technologies described are effective when practiced accurately and regularly. They are not to replace medical treatment where indicated. Results will vary with individuals. Consult your physician before starting any new physical exercise.

Love (Prem)

Love is an Ocean, endless and unfathomable.
Love is the constant churning of the butter of the Nam.
Love is the endless taste of the Infinite.
Love, O Love! is the strength of God.
Love is the life support of the Soul.
Love makes the world go around.
In Love lives the Lord of the Universe.
Love's devotion makes you radiant.
Love is only understood by the lover.
The lover enjoys the ecstasy of the Infinite.
Love is Union, and deep meditation.
The whole Universe is made of Love.

O Yogi! Love God!
And lovingly sing His loving praises,
For whoever loves God as the Doer of everything,
Escapes the pain of death.
Love, O Yogi! is what you are!
So chant Sat Nam and Sat Kartar!

– Yogi Bhajan, *Furmaan Khalsa*

Forward by Dr. Dharma Singh Khalsa, M.D.

Sex is great. Great sex is fantastic. There is nothing more ecstatic, however, than sacred sex, enjoyed within the foundation of a spiritual relationship. In *The Art of Making Sex Sacred*, Guru Terath Kaur Khalsa, Ph.D., draws from ancient wisdom and modern psychology to guide us on a path of creating spiritual relationships. Today, more than ever before, it is notable that honest, loving, spiritual relationships are linked to successful aging, longevity, and peace of mind.

Although Guru Terath Kaur has done a great deal of research in preparation for this book, she is not writing from a dry academic point of view. She is writing from personal experience and wisdom.

In *The Art of Making Sex Sacred*, many timely topics are presented, including nutrition and diet, meditation techniques to bring each person to an exalted state, the practical approach of massage to heighten couple sensitivity, and yoga exercises to increase sexual energy. All of these techniques work together to increase intimacy and bring the practitioner to a state of bliss before, during, and after making love.

As humanity moves from the Pisean Age to the Age of Aquarius, and from the 20th to the 21st century, we need books like this to soothe an otherwise intense transition. In my own work with patients suffering from many of the illnesses of our day, which I have written about in my books, *Brain Longevity, The Pain Cure,* and *Divine Well Being*, I can tell you that we need to deepen our spiritual connections. Those who do so will love, live, thrive, and survive. Those who are unable or unwilling to do so, will face deep loneliness, cold depression, severe pain, and premature death. We are all so blessed to have a book like this to help us create true and loving spiritual relationships which are the keys to optimal health and happiness.

Dharma Singh Khalsa, M.D.
Tucson, Arizona

Dharma Singh Khalsa, M.D. is the author of *Brain Longevity* (Warner Books), a breakthrough medical program that improves your mind and memory. He is also a longtime student of Yogi Bhajan.

From the Author

In my lifetime, I have watched society go through tremendous changes. Growing up in Southern California in the early 1950's, television was just becoming a household item. My grandmother lived across the street; my friends and I played fearlessly in a small neighborhood where we knew nearly everyone and watched out for one another.

Forty years later, the human need for love and trust is still essential. The world we live in, however, has changed dramatically. In our fast-paced world, it has become increasingly difficult to have a lasting, intimate relationship. We spend long hours at the workplace or commuting on freeways. We are in a constant race to make ends meet. Technology has made our communication more efficient, but it often isolates us from more personal, authentic relationships. For most of us, extended family is represented by a faded photograph on the wall. Our neighborhoods are filled with strangers living behind locked doors.

Out of isolation and alienation, many people are seeking deeper meaning in their lives. There is an upward surge of interest in spiritual pursuits. Prayer has become an accepted therapy in the treatment of life-threatening illness, and meditation is employed in the treatment of depression, phobias and low-self-esteem.

In 1970, I took my first Kundalini Yoga class. I have lived and taught the practices and teachings on which this book is based for over 28 years. These teachings encompass a lifestyle that enriches every aspect of life, including sexual relationships. My spiritual teacher, Harbhajan Singh Khalsa Yogiji, Ph.D. (known as Yogi Bhajan) is the humble and dynamic messenger of these remarkable teachings. He arrived from India in the turmoil of the late 1960's to share the ancient sacred science of Kundalini Yoga for the upliftment of humanity. Kundalini Yoga is the Science of Awareness, working directly on your total energy, body, mind and soul, including sexual energy.

The Art of Making Sex Sacred was inspired from my own marriage and from listening to hundreds of my Kundalini Yoga workshop

participants and counseling clients who are seeking a way to bring spirituality into their lives and intimate relationships. This book is a gift and
a gem, and the teachings are authentic and effective. Practiced with
devotion and consistency, the techniques in this book have the power to
transform and heal, but they are not meant to replace professional care
when needed.

I suggest you read this book from cover to cover, then try out a few
of the techniques that interest you. Once you understand the basic con-
cepts, you will probably want to return to your favorite sections. The
teachings are an art and a science and as such should be practiced with
reverence and respect. To further your understanding about all these
techniques, including Kundalini Yoga, check the Resource section on
page 119 for information on Kundalini Yoga classes in your area.

Personal growth work is a journey and the results do not happen
immediately. Work on changing and elevating your own consciousness
and let God do the rest. Approach all of your efforts with an attitude of
gratitude, patience, and positivity. Above all, have fun, be adventurous,
relax, and enjoy the unfoldment of your Being.

Guru Terath Kaur Khalsa, Ph.D.
Espanola, New Mexico

TABLE OF CONTENTS

Table of Contents

INTRODUCTION TO *THE ART OF MAKING SEX SACRED*

Sex and sexuality are prevalent topics in the 90's. The aura of sex sells everything from designer jeans to milk! Yet for all the "air-time" sex receives, it is still a mystifying subject to most of us. What most of us are truly seeking is intimacy, meaningful connection, and fulfillment, which are perhaps at the heart of this preoccupation with sex. The concept of sacred sex represents the reclaiming our role as divine beings merging through intimate communion with God.

In the Eastern traditions, sexuality was taught as an art and a science. The knowledge of the fundamentals and principles of sexuality contributed to the hallmark of a truly enlightened person. The Western world, in the 20th Century, evolved the science of psychology to aid in the personal discovery of self. Together, in *The Art of Making Sex Sacred,* East and West merge in the technology of sacred sexuality, and allow us to experience our oneness with the cosmos.

The Art of Making Sex Sacred is a guidebook to restoring the lost art of sex as a spiritual practice. For centuries, sex was revered as a sacred act. What we have lost over the ages can be regained by applying the techniques of Kundalini Yoga, diet, and meditation, as taught by Yogi Bhajan, who has

"The sexual union is actually and absolutely divine, because the experience one has during sex is the same as the experience of God consciousness." – Yogi Bhajan

1

taught this sacred science in the West since 1969. In this sex manual for students of spirituality, Guru Terath Kaur Khalsa, Ph.D., a long-time student of Yogi Bhajan, psychologist and counselor, compiles a manual of yogic sexual techniques for expanded consciousness, with their powerful ability to transform and heal.

Seekers of spiritual bliss will find information in this manual for gaining self-awareness, rejuvenating one's sexual health and rebuilding intimacy. Included are meditations and exercises for couples to enhance communications, support healing and allow the experience of blissful lovemaking. There is a chapter describing special foods for men and women designed to enhance the experience of ecstasy and fulfillment through sex.

Within the dance of life, there is the act of sex, which is the merging of our beings into the lifeforce of the creation. More than just a lust or passion for another person on a purely physical level, sex is a truly sacred act of Nature and God. This manual seeks to help those who are on that path of discovery to find their way home into the arms of the true beloved.

CHAPTER 1

THE POWER OF ATTRACTION

What can explain the powerful attraction between the sexes? According to Master of Kundalini Yoga, Yogi Bhajan, it is the longing to belong to another, to merge with the essence of one's polarity, that defines our search for love. He says:

"Consider a young man in his twenties, who meets a young woman, and they fall in love. There is a very powerful feeling that is called longing for each other. This instinct of longing is the most powerful instinct, because it can prevent the totality of the psyche of the universe from acting in relation and according to the individual psyche...There is no way you can understand the impact and the depth of this relationship."

"The most powerful unknown power of the individual can be realized in one relationship only – the relationship between male and female." – Yogi Bhajan

SPERMATOZOA AND EGG

With this longing and this instinct to merge, why does it seem that men and women are so far apart? Physiology explains part of the "Venus vs. Mars" syndrome. After all, a man's sexual organs are on the outside. His nature tends to be the seeker of new horizons to conquer and master. Man is the seeder, producing millions of spermatozoa that zigzag like a snake toward the object of their desire (the egg) circling eight times around before penetrating the mystery of life, catalyzing the creation of a new being.

Woman represents the heart of mystery and secrets. Her organs are on the inside, creating the womb of life. Her body produces only one egg per moon cycle. She calls upon the lifeforce to enter her sacred space. Then, when she is ready, her body furnishes the nourishing environment for a new soul to re-enter the circle of birth, life, death and rebirth. Together, man and woman are the tree of life on which future generations depend. The polarity of the sexes decides the destiny of humanity.

In yogic philosophy, male and female are the sun and the moon. The ego, fixed and hard, protects the man's seed from destruction. Female, patient and yielding, is the fluid that carries the seed to its destiny. Later, woman turns her blood into milk, to feed the child. The sacrifice of blood and sweat are the waters of life which guarantee its continuation.

NURTURERS AND CONQUERORS

It is true that both female and male qualities exist in everyone. There are men who are more nurturing than others, and women who are exploring new frontiers. Generally, these are tendencies. The woman who is the pioneer can still have the inclination to nurture her new frontiers. It is important that we learn how to balance, appreciate, and utilize the two energies. In fact, the flow of energy between opposite poles of male and female is the key to harmonizing the flow of energy in one's life. It is based on the natural law of the universe that positive and negative forces attract and bond with each other, like a pair of magnets locking together. In the West, this concept of opposite energies has become common in holistic health, but has not, yet, been understood in terms of sexuality.

The Taoists describe it with the simple metaphor of cooking. Yang is fire and Yin is water. Man is the fire, and woman is the water. When a man makes love with a woman, he cooks the woman's water in her vagina with his penis, which is fire. The woman is usually sexually stronger, for her water puts out the male's fire and his erection loses its flame. Yin, soft and yielding, always conquers Yang, hard and unyielding.

To most in our society, sex is a release and nothing more. However, the highest sexual relationship is an absolute worship, reverence, devotion and love, where the auras and subtle bodies merge. The circle of energy cannot connect if a man only joins his penis with a woman's vagina, without loving her with his heart. Both the lower chakras and the higher ones must be joined for the flow of energy to be complete. When the upper poles of man and woman are joined at the heart and mouth as well as the genitals, then the magnet can become an electromagnetic dynamo. If man and woman use their ability to channel the energy up to their higher centers through meditation and love, they can experience a spiritual union, which transcends any personal pleasure or ego satisfaction. They will obtain a different state of being, which can be a high state of spiritual awareness and healing. It can become the worship of divinity in the temple of their lover's body.

That is why there must be a marital commitment to one another before God. And, in order to enjoy married life, there must be an atmosphere of genuine trust and devotion. To reach that state, each person must understand their depth and dimension. This means that one must examine and experience the depths of their consciousness and explore the extent and height of their potential, as well as pitfalls and limitations. It means looking closely at one's priorities and commitments.

KUNDALINI COIL OF THE BELOVED

Human beings require pranic energy to live. The yogis teach that at birth each one of us is granted a certain number of breaths to breathe. When we respect the life force energy, by channeling the pranic energy through proper breathing and use of the body's energy, we can live long, healthy lives. Disrespect of the prana, through wanton sex, poor diet, and lack of devotion, shortens our lifespan and the quality of life suffers.

Sex is the ultimate physical union. Sex also nurtures the life force energy. Kundalini Yoga, the science of awareness, is a powerful technology that teaches the proper use of all our energies (including sexual energy). Through yogic practice, each person can experience the potency, vitality and heightened consciousness that is their human birthright. The power to attract goodness, love, health, prosperity and peace, comes from having a radiant aura and a healthy, balanced, centered life. A worshipful attitude flows from a healthy and happy existence, allowing sacredness to enter every facet of our lives and to fill us with greater meaning and pleasure.

CHAPTER 2

WOMAN AND MAN

Men and women have different dimensions. A man is like a flowing river, sometimes shallow, sometimes deep. A woman is a deep, deep lake; so deep that she can not find her own bottom. Nevertheless, once the process begins, a spiritual man and woman, united in the eyes of God, can continue diving into the depths of their consciousness for a lifetime, discovering new depths and meanings. They also need to understand each other's dimensions.

POLARITY

"Woman's dimension should be as vast as the sky, covering everything and shining on the dark night. Her sweetness, her endurance and the words she speaks should ever be right. When a woman speaks it is very rhythmical to man, it is very soothing and loving." – *Yogi Bhajan*

Men and women are not the same, not equal; they are perfect polarities and compliment each other when freedom is given to live to their true essences. These basic natures also reflect the needs of the man and woman. As the seeder, the male goes out to conquer. His ego is greater than a female's, which he needs when he goes out into the world. It is the male essence. At the end of the day, the man needs a place to retreat at night. His home

"The relationship is between Purkha and Prakirti, not between a woman and a man. A man who does not see Prakirti (goddess) in a woman will never find strength to see the infinity of God. And a female who doesn't find the nucleus of God in a man will never have the ecstasy of divine experience."
– Yogi Bhajan

7

is a refuge, where he looks to the female to nurture and inspire him. He wants support and encouragement, so he can go out into the world again the next day.

SECURITY

"A woman needs security of the future because she conceives, gets pregnant and has children to raise and she needs emotional security. That is why the institution of marriage is essential." – Yogi Bhajan

The female requires security and protection, which the man provides. It is in her genetic programming as mother to seek this protection for the life she will bear. Individually, the woman may have a better paying job than her mate, she may have a black belt in karate. It does not matter. The male must be the leader, the constant sun, the unwavering support. If he does not provide the security, within the female grows insecurity, harshness, and resentment that hinder the manifestation of her natural essence.

Our society has lost sight of what men and women are and what they need from each other. A woman may also be out in the world, but her power and greatness will come out as a woman there, not as a pseudo-man. There is nothing more powerful and beautiful than a woman who uses her graceful capabilities to accomplish the job she sets out to do. Moreover, there is nothing more grand than a man, who is not afraid to be a man, with humility and focused determination.

Men and women are not equal, but they are equally perfect in their essences. Until this is recognized and reflected in respectful and conscious behavior towards each other, there won't be harmony between the sexes.

RESPECT FOR WOMAN

"There is no peace on this earth because woman is not respected. If man is born of a woman, he must respect her. If a tree is separated from its roots, how can it live? When you do not respect a woman, you lose the root of your intelligence, of your spirit, because woman is the spirit." – Yogi Bhajan

When intercourse happens, the auras blend. The man feels the woman's energy in his aura for one month, from moon to moon. He has the capacity to implant his spermatozoa into many women, without the same depths of emotional effect that the woman experiences. The woman, conversely, contains the man's energy in her aura more intensely for a longer period. Any relationship with a male goes deep into her soul, and it can stay with her for a long time. She gives part of herself to the man, and what she gets in return is a soul, which is born through her womb. This is the nature of the mother.

For this reason, it is of utmost importance that there is commitment in the relationship and purity of consciousness. When she has intercourse, she can use her purity to either create another soul in the form of a baby, or give these vibrations to her husband. Whether unconsciously or consciously, he will receive the vibrations that will affect his consciousness and energy. The man will seek that energy repeatedly, because it is satisfying on all levels.

SPIRIT AND RELATIONSHIP

Normally the man loses energy after he ejaculates. If the woman's aura is weak or non-existent, or if her energy is purely lustful and emanating from her second chakra, he will feel totally drained. On the other hand, if the woman, who is Spirit, relates from her heart and higher centers, and if her aura is bright and extends nine feet during lovemaking, the man will feel nurtured and blessed. Kundalini Yoga and meditation are effective ways to purify the aura of past relationships and to strengthen it for the present one.

Sexual intercourse is not a relationship between the penis and vagina. It is total merger of polarities, auras, spirits and consciousness. Appreciating this can bring a blissful merger for both partners on the highest spiritual level. Sex is a sacred act, which, if done consciously, can take the couple to the consciousness of Infinity within them. Sex should be a creative force, according to Yogi Bhajan, to absolutely regenerate the couple, the family, the surroundings and the Self.

The ancient, Oriental understanding of man and woman as the yin and yang polarity is as old as yoga itself. It originates from a deep awareness of male and female energies, which exists within us, and which can serve us, if we honor and protect them through our psyches and spiritual practice.

THE MOON CENTERS – As taught by Yogi Bhajan

According to yogic teachings, a woman has eleven lunar centers, which activate in her body in a 28-day cycle, spending 2-1/2 days at each location in the body. The sequence varies with each woman, but unless there is an emotional shock, it remains constant in her. They do not coincide with her menstrual cycle or zodiacal moon cycle. If the woman is sensitive to her body and emotional tendencies, she can be aware of and predict her own moon cycle. With sensitive observation, a man can also follow a woman's moon cycle.

A man also has one moon center, on the chin. If a man has a beard, he will be steady and constant in his behavior. The man's moon center remains constant, unlike the eleven moon centers of the woman. If a man is sensitive to a woman's moon cycle, he can also appropriately adjust his behavior. When would be the best time to buy her flowers, or approach her about a controversial topic? When would be the most optimal time to have sex?

The woman's emotions will fluctuate as the moon centers change. When it is in the **clitoris** or **vagina**, she is charming, talkative, sociable and outgoing. Clitoris is a great time to wear a new dress to a party, make new friends, network, make telephone sales, and go to a PTA meeting or a bake sale – anything in a crowd or social situation. She will shine like a star. She shouldn't balance her checkbook or try to figure out what's wrong with her marriage at this time.

When the moon center is in the lower organs or in the **thighs**, she is very confirming and wants to substantiate everything. It is at this time that she wants to get things done and feels productive. All of the details, which may slip during the rest of the month, seem like they have to be

Hairline
Eyebrows
Cheeks
Ear Lobes
Lips
Back of Neck

Breasts

Navel

Clitoris
Vagina

Inner Thighs

MOON CENTERS

done during this time, almost to the point of obsession. The thighs are a good time to put into action all the things she has dreamed about changing this month.

"I can always tell if I am in the thigh center, because even though I may be making love with my husband, I am still making lists in my head and thinking about all the things I need to do." – W.K.K.

When it is in the **navel** or corresponding spot on the spine, she is the most insecure and very vulnerable to criticism. This is a good time for her to strengthen her navel center with Sat Kriya or Breath of Fire (see Chapter 5). If her navel center is strong, she can feel more assertive and powerful. Navel is a good time to keep a diary, log thoughts, chant loudly for 31 minutes, find a friend to make her laugh at her faults or inconsistencies.

When it is in her **breasts**, she is compassionate, heart-centered, intimate and giving to the extent of foolishness. During this time, she has the hardest time creating boundaries in her life. She may agree to things to which she would normally say "no." If she has unclear goals or low self-esteem, this can be a foolish time for her, although not necessarily dangerous. Breasts are a good time to throw a party, go to lunch, buy a present, give a birthday call, or visit a lonely friend.

When it is at the **back of the neck**, she is very romantic, in fact, one little flower or gesture can make her go nuts. She will take risks, she is flirtatious, not just with men, but with life in general. Her personality is whimsical, not logical. Back of the neck is a good time to try new things, like flirting with ideas and people, as long as she isn't too serious about the results. It is a bad time for meetings, planning sessions, and careful work.

When the moon center is at the **lips**, a woman's communication is either very effective or ineffective. Much depends upon her diet. If she is eating a good diet and is clearing her subconscious mind through meditation, her communication will be uplifting, powerful and effectual. If she is not eating a good diet and is mentally off center, her speech will be harsh, hurtful and unproductive.

A very dangerous time may occur when it is around the **pinks of the cheeks**. Losing its peacefulness, her mind flirts with danger and goes out of control. This is the time she would be reactionary, commotional and crazy. The characteristics of this moon center may resemble Pre-menstral Syndrome (PMS). Moreover, if this moon center happens at the same time as her PMS or period, it can be an overwhelmingly difficult time for her. She could destroy her marriage, alienate her children or her co-workers. All obsessions and demons haunt her at this time. Pink of the cheeks is a good time to pray for God's grace to help her out of the ridiculous situation in which she finds herself.

At the **earlobes**, she may discuss values and what's important to her. She sees all of the right and wrong in the world and is very moralistic. She may just be aware of this injustice or she may act on it by writing her Congressman or join a political rally. She analyzes her own personality traits, as well as everything around her.

She is very imaginative and illusionary when her moon center is in the **eyebrows**. Used in a constructive way, this is a good time to write a poem, plan a party or a romantic vacation, play with a child, and brainstorm a new idea or dream of being the next superstar. Her ideas go beyond the ordinary. This would not, however, be the best time to go on an expensive shopping spree (she would buy the store out) or act on her outrageous ideas. Wait for thighs!

At the **hairline** (arcline), she is at her best. She is outgoing, centered, authoritative, sensitive, all knowing and neutral in her communication. The hairline follows the pathway of the arcline, or halo; woman is the closest to her truth when her moon is in the hairline. She feels confident and self-assured. The arcline is the nucleus of the aura. It goes from earlobe to earlobe over the head. It is the arcline which we call the halo in our pictures of saints. When the arcline is strong, one is projective. One's thoughts can become reality. Woman has two arclines, the second one connecting between the nipples of the breasts. As mother, God gave her this second arcline as a protective shield for her child and as an extra protection for the mother's health and power. There is nothing more protective than a mother of her children.

If a woman watches her diet, exercises, practices yoga, meditates, and maintains a positive attitude, she can observe her emotional tendencies at each moon center but not be a victim to them. She can study them to better understand her personality and then use them for her benefit. For example, when a woman knows she needs to make an important decision, she might hesitate until her moon cycle passes out of the navel center or cheeks. Her energy will be more stable when it passes into the clitoris or hairline. On the other hand, if she wants to write a poem, it might be better to wait until the eyebrows come around.

Yogi Bhajan stresses that a healthy diet can prevent imbalances in the moon centers during puberty, menopause, pregnancy, and any other times a woman's hormones are changing. He also says that a female fetus experiences her moon centers in the womb, from the moment she becomes female.

"Whenever I feel overwhelmed by my emotions, I keep in mind that they will pass within two days anyway. It sometimes amazes me how much my emotions fluctuate. I try to be patient and not take them so seriously." – W.K.K.

CELEBRATING OUR DIFFERENCES

"Women are exactly opposite from men. They have nothing in common. It is only the mysterious thing called 'love' which brings them together." – Yogi Bhajan

As men and women in relationships, we must strive to celebrate the differences between us that can strengthen and complement each other's abilities. Whereas a woman has great intuitive faculties (she is 16 times more intuitive than a man, according to Yogi Bhajan), a man has a great capacity for constancy. For both sexes, we must never lose our direction towards that ultimate Unity, which is God. Within each gender is the germ or seed of the opposite polarity, which attracts us toward each other. By merging ourselves with our Other, we can experience wholeness of being through the unique blending of the male and female essences.

MEDITATION FOR BALANCING MOON CENTERS
(For Women Only)

This meditation balances the woman' s moon centers, her menstrual cycle, and her zodiac moon cycle. It also balances the glandular system. It is one of the most creative and highest meditations for a woman. If practiced for 40 days or more, she can break any habit.

Lying on the stomach, place the chin on the ground, and keep the head straight. The arms should be along side the body, with the palms of the hands facing upwards.

The Panj Shabad, **SAA, TAA, NAA, MAA,** is the mantra used for this meditation.

SAA – Infinity, cosmos, beginning

TAA – Life, existence

NAA – Death, totality

MAA – Rebirth, resurrection

Chant the mantra silently, while the eyes are focused at the brow point. Meditate on the sound current coming in through the crown of the head and flowing out through the third eye point, creating an "L."

As you mentally repeat the vibration of **SAA** firmly press the tip of the index finger to the tip of the thumb; on **TAA** press the tip of the middle finger to the thumb; on **NAA** press the tip of the ring finger to the thumb; and on **MAA** press the tip of the little finger to the thumb.

The breath will regulate itself. Continue in this manner from 3–31 minutes.

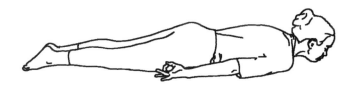

The Art of Making Sex Sacred

CHAPTER 3

BUILDING INTIMACY

Sex does not necessarily come with intimacy and intimacy often does not come with sex; however, intimacy should be at the core of a relationship in order to experience true spiritual sex. Intimacy implies a deep, interpersonal relationship based on trust, sharing, and mutual respect. Through intimacy, we can touch the soulful, inner core of our being. Through sexual intimacy, we can heal ourselves of the fear of letting another person see our innermost selves.

"If you are not aware of someone else, then in reality you are not aware of yourself." – Yogi Bhajan

WANTING GREATER INTIMACY

Feelings of isolation during sex often come from one partner wanting a more intimate sexual relationship. It is often heard, "My partner thinks our relationship is fine just the way it is; but it's going to take both of us to bring about change." Nevertheless, it is not necessary for both partners to work towards redefining the relationship in order for it to happen.

Women and men often have different needs in a sexual relationship. A woman can feel incomplete if she relates to sex purely on a physical level. Women and men want their sexual relationship to be emotionally fulfilling and spiritually uplifting. Because men and women often have different needs, it is important to find out what is fulfilling for yourself and for your partner. If one or both partners desire a more fulfilling sexual relationship it can happen. If one partner changes his or her attitude and role, the relationship will change. If a person identifies their need for greater intimacy, it is often helpful to begin the process without involving the other partner in the process, until one's self-esteem makes it possible to experiment with letting down the guard. Change can often be threatening to a relationship, but if one person starts the process it can enable the other partner to feel safer about exploring vulnerable topics. Here are some steps towards building or rebuilding intimacy in your relationship.

CLAIM YOUR POWER

The first step in building intimacy is to claim your power. What this means for many people who are unhappy in their relationships is to determine if you are playing the victim and then mentally change your attitude from being a victim to being in control. You need to claim your power in order to be in control of your life. We are never helpless, only the mind makes us think so.

How do you feel your power? Start with Kundalini Yoga and meditation (see Chapter 5). Yoga and meditation open a person up to their vitality, clarity and creativity. Move your energy up through your lower chakras, opening and releasing from old self-destructive blocks. Once you start to clear away the negative, self-destructive thought patterns, you will start to feel different. When you begin to feel the fire of your inner vitality, your mind will begin to function with a new clarity. Your creativity will find expanded expression. Let intuition be your guide, rather than the commotion of fluctuating emotions.

When you begin the process of building your self-esteem, you will behave differently. You will assert yourself and your needs in a manner that may scare or intimidate your partner. Even if your relationship has been "on the rocks," or lacking that "certain something," it is common for people to want to maintain the status quo. The unknown is often frightening, especially when it comes to sharing intimate, sexual

18

moments that could expose deep, untouched emotions. At this time, if one partner starts to build the trust with loving, non-accusing communication, a closer relationship can begin to develop.

POSITIVE PROJECTION

Your negative mind can be your best friend (warning you of potential dangers). It can also be an enemy to change (telling you that change is scary and should be avoided). After you have begun addressing your self-esteem issues and reclaiming your power, you will start to tune into how your negative mind tries to sabotage the change process. At this time, you must be positive in your projection, to give the relationship a chance to be nurtured without fear.

Staying positive may be difficult at this time, but it is essential. Keep a sense of humor about the little things that are not as important as they seem. Intimacy takes time. You may feel super-sensitive about the way your partner looks, acts, or talks. Try not to over-analyze every little nuance—look at the Big Picture. Tell yourself, "This is an important relationship I am nurturing." Reversing old habit patterns can be painful and slow. For every movement forward ("He finally understands why I hate it when he touches me that way!") there will probably be retreats back into the "Dark Age" of your sex life ("She knows I like this type of sex, but she never wants to do it my way!"). Now is the time to visualize the best about your partner and your relationship.

In your meditation, picture your mate as a radiant spiritual being. Surround your partner with light and energy. Make time for each other, and show interest in your partner's life and accomplishments. Appreciate your mate even by noticing something that seems obvious or mundane. Be light and playful. That energy will lure your partner into wanting to play. Above all, keep up and stay positive. When you have a negative thought, cut that thought with a positive affirmation. Project that the outcome will be positive.

FOREPLAY IS "FOR PLAY"

When you are working to create intimacy, you need a setting for your divine play. Plan your next date with your mate. Though it may seem like a lot of work, and kind of strange if you aren't used to planning your sexual encounters, plan a romantic, fun-filled, intimate experience. It does not need to include sex. It might even be better if it does not include sex at first, to take off the pressure. The important thing in building intimacy is to create an atmosphere of coziness. You do not have to tell your partner what you are planning to do. Either partner can be the initiator. Go on a hike. Give him a foot or back massage. Serve a candlelit dinner. Start a conversation. Send her flowers and poetry. Listen to her without criticism, giving advice or trying to fix anything. Open, honest and heartfelt communication is important. Find out what your partner enjoys and needs. Hugs, holding hands, kisses and touching are some of the most important ways to communicate. Getting out of your head and into the action is an important step at this stage of intimacy building.

"My wife and I have been married 39 years. Our sexual relationship has not always been good, largely due to poor communication. Over time, we developed a special system of communication. We write back and forth to each other. One of us will write about a subject and give it to the other, who then responds in writing. Later, we discuss it. This system has helped us communicate our thoughts and feelings about delicate subjects." – George (yoga student)

SETTING THE SCENE

Creating an environment for intimacy to flourish is part of the art of sacred sex. Just as you create a sacred space for meditation, you need to create an aura of spiritual peace and beauty. Place flowers in the room, light a candle, select uplifting music, and prepare the special ginger milk drink (see Appendix A: Sexy Foods). Arrange for the children to spend the night with a friend or grandparents. For a man, this preparation creates a nurturing space, almost like a womb. For a woman, the sacred ritual of preparation releases the creative energy that anchors her to her "Shakti" or primal feminine power. A woman can create that energy for her partner, not as a mother, but as a woman. Do it from your heart, with love and watch him respond in kind. Don't create any expectations about what that response will be. This is a time to surrender old expectations, fears, and pride. If one partner isn't interested in having sex, it can help build the trust when the relationship is allowed to develop without force.

SLOW IT DOWN

Intimacy is a deepening of a relationship on so many levels. In our modern, hectic world, we do not understand the fine art of patience. Women are just as guilty as men in allowing the sexual act to become a race against the clock. Usually a man will not slow the lovemaking process, so the woman needs to help her partner to take more time. This does not need words. Develop an enjoyable and fulfilling experience of exploring each other's bodies. Be subtle. Go into the deep, meditative experience of it. If you can, start with a meditation and a Venus Kriya (see Chapter 7). Take a long time to massage all the erotic points (see Chapter 8). Disconnect from the world of schedules and timeclocks. Make sex sacred because it is the key to the spiritual healing and bonding of two bodies into one soul.

HEALING AND TRUST

Lack of trust and intimacy between two people often comes from past hurts and betrayals that occurred before the relationship began. Other times the mistrust comes from betrayals of one or both partners during the relationship. These betrayals are very difficult to heal. It is easiest if both want healing, but, even in damaged relationships, there is hope even if only one partner makes the effort.

Psychologist Milton Erikson tells a story about trust. A married couple came to him for hypnotherapy and counseling. The problem was that no matter how many times the husband told his wife that he loved her, she would not believe him. Under hypnosis, it was revealed that on their honeymoon night they had had an argument. During that argument, her husband told her that he was sorry he married her. Soon after, they made up and, supposedly, everything was fine. However, from that time on she would not trust her husband's signs of love and affection for her. Erikson instructed the husband that the next time his wife climaxed during lovemaking he was to tell her in a very emotional, loving way that he loved her and has always loved her. No further therapy was necessary.

The human heart is a powerfully resilient organ. When we begin to trust and open our hearts, miracles truly happen.

CHAPTER 4

THE JOURNEY OF SELF-AWARENESS

The journey of self-awareness marks the beginning of finding the core of spirituality in our true nature. There are many techniques and philosophies related to this subject. In this chapter, we will explore the interwoven aspects meditation, affirmation, and self-love that are the foundations of our ability to connect significantly to others.

MEDITATION AND SELF-ESTEEM

Meditation is a very private, internal experience that a person has with his or her inner Self. It is an important technique in the quest for sacred sexuality. Meditation improves self-esteem and heals emotional wounds, allowing the development of self-awareness that can lead to a heart-centered opening in the love relationship with one's self or with another person. Meditation also connects one to one's Soul, and balances the yin (female) and yang (male) energies in the body. Certain meditations can enhance the feeling of ecstasy experienced during sex.

INTIMACY WITH ONESELF

"Ignoring your soul is ignoring your Godhead. As a rose has an aroma, so you have a soul; as a mirror has an image, so you have a soul. Ignoring your soul is ignoring your total capacity."—Yogi Bhajan

"Meditation is a duty toward the self. The moment you become aware of the self you become beautiful to the self because the moment you concentrate on self, your frequency changes and the universe around you changes also. This is a cosmic law." –Yogi Bhajan

23

Before one can truly enjoy an intimate relationship with another person, one has to develop an intimate relationship with one's own Self. We need to develop all the qualities of intimacy within our self and ask, "Do I trust myself, accept myself, nurture myself, and honor myself? Can I be vulnerable, honest and open with myself?" Intimacy with one's self can only develop from the inside. It has nothing to do with being with or doing for anyone else. It has everything to do with being with your Soul. Instead of being anxious to make another person your beloved, first make your Soul your Beloved. This relationship is the most important one in your life, because it will never abandon or betray you.

Meditation, affirmation, and visualization are powerful tools for connecting with your soul. A positive affirmation is "God and Me, Me and God, Are One." Recite it verbally or silently to yourself, any time, all the time. As you repeat it, feel in harmony with your inner Self. Whenever you have a negative thought, blast it with this powerful affirmation. Visualize yourself as pure light or an angelic being, and then connect to that image.

"Start understanding that you are the creative source and nucleus of the whole vibratory effect. The moment you understand that, your problem is solved. The moment you know that you are you, your problems are over. The moment you know that you are you, God and you are one, because you are the Creator and He is the Creator." – Yogi Bhajan

Personal affirmations are powerful. State them in the present, clearly defined and totally positive. (Example: "I am healthy and happy now.") Use the creativity of your mind in the form of visualizations to make your affirmations even more empowering. Put all of your senses into your visualization. How does it look, smell, sound and feel?

As you feel connected to your inner Self, your self-love will grow. Loving yourself from within is crucial to having a healthy sexual relationship. We have to love and believe in ourselves, so that we can love from a confident place, instead of a needy one.

Meditation is only one way to tune into your inner source. Take time now to write down the ways you already make that connection, such as hiking in the mountains, walking on the beach, smelling flowers, swimming in the ocean, playing music, singing, dancing, painting or watching a sunset. Whichever way you choose, allow your inner intimacy to grow and flourish, until you are ready to share it with someone else. That other may come in the form of a parent, a child, a friend or a life-long partner. When intimacy is the core of a sexual relationship, your bliss and healing will be limitless.

"Spirituality is an individual thing. First, you stand alone with God. Then you and your partner can stand together with God. Have self-respect; don't use others and never allow yourself to be used unrighteously. Let there be a privacy and a sacredness to your spirituality and your sexuality." – *Marge (yoga student).*

LOVING YOUR BODY

Loving ourselves from the inside and having an intimate relationship with our Inner Beloved is the foundation of a happy, sacred life. Moreover, in order to have a healthy sex life, we also have to love our physical bodies. Loving and appreciating our bodies helps us to feel more comfortable when expressing our sensual and sexual selves. Most of us have been conditioned by childhood, school, religious, and cultural experiences to be extremely critical of ourselves, especially of our bodies. The negative programming in our heads feeds us with degrading thoughts about our body's size, shape and condition. Television, movies, and magazines all present us with the skinny, sexy, social image. Our dress, projection and presence also give a message. Stand before the mirror and ask yourself, "What am I dressing for – sex or spirit?" In "dressing for Venus and not for penis," a woman can experience her total radiance as a Grace of God. Yogi Bhajan, in his inspiring lectures on women's spirituality, tells women to dress well, behave gracefully and learn the art of presenting themselves. Look graceful so that a person will relate to your grace and not your sexuality. If you don't have a price tag (i.e. your body is not on sale) and you make your price Infinity, you shall merge with Infinity.

Here is an exercise to help you learn how to love your body. Choose a private time and space for yourself. Play some soothing music and light a candle or incense. Take a shower or bath and dry off in front of the mirror. Begin to massage each part of your body with oil or lotion. As you massage each part of you body, thank it for how it has served you. For example, "Thank you Feet for carrying me all the miles of my life." "Thank you Hips for supporting me and giving me stability." "Thank you Nose for being able to smell the roses." "Thank you Breasts for giving nourishment to my babies." Be creative. If a negative thought pattern slips into your mind, take a deep breath and dispel it with a positive affirmation.

After you feel comfortable doing this part of the exercise, massage each part of your body and tune into your sensuality and sexuality. Go as slowly as you need to stay within your comfort zone. Be kind to yourself. Allow any feelings that come up. Embrace your emotions as a natural, beautiful, and sacred part of your being.

When you finish, acknowledge your Self as a Grace of God (woman) or as a Man of God (male). When we exalt our True Selves, we limit the amount of mental, physical or emotional abuse (from ourselves and others) that we are willing to receive. We open ourselves with trust and humility to the Boundless Love that surrounds us.

MEDITATION NOTES

The following section will guide you in the basics of some simple meditation techniques. When meditating, it is best to choose a place that is clean, quiet, and without distractions. Wear loose clothing, and sit in a comfortable position with the spine straight, either cross-legged or in a chair. If you sit in a chair, make sure your feet are uncrossed and flat on the floor with your weight evenly distributed.

You can also sit on your heels in Rock Pose (see figure right). For some meditations, you may lie flat on your back in a relaxed position sometimes called corpse pose.

TUNING IN

Before meditating, "tune in" to your sacred center. Do some deep breathing to slow the mind and body. As you inhale, scan the body for tension. As you exhale, let the tension go. If possible, do some Kundalini Yoga exercises beforehand to set the glandular and nervous system, so you can experience a deep sense of peace and tranquility (see Chapter 5).

The mantra used before practicing any Kundalini Yoga exercise or meditation is **ONG NAMO GURU DEV NAMO**, which means "I bow to the Creator, I bow to the Divine Teacher within." With your eyes closed, take a few long, deep breaths, tuning into the meaning and vibration of the mantra. Call upon your Higher Teacher to guide your journey of healing and self-awareness. Repeat the mantra 3 to 5 times. Next, chant the following mantra three times for protection: **AAD GURAY NAMEH, JUGAAD GURAY NAMEH, SAAT GURAY NAMEH, SIREE GURU DAYV-AY NAMEH.** Chant each repetition in a monotone on just one breath. Protection and guidance are always with us, but sometimes we are unaware of it. This mantra clears the way to open ourselves to the sources of wisdom and teaching that are already within us. Chant these two mantras before practicing any Kundalini Yoga exercises (*kriyas*), meditations, or *Venus Kriyas* (see Chapters 5 and 7).

HAND MUDRAS

Hand positions or mudras create a specific result – they change the neuro-chemical balance of the brain. Most meditations use *gyan mudra* (gii-ahn moo-dra), by touching the tips of the index fingers to the tips of the thumbs. Gyan mudra is used for invoking divine wisdom. The elbows are straight with the back of the hands resting on the knees. The other fingers are straight. Other mudras may be specified in the following meditations, or in the section on Venus Kriyas (see Chapter 7).

EYE FOCUS

There is generally a specified focus for the eyes. Typically, when meditating the eyes are closed with the focus at a spot between the eyebrows known in yogic terms as the ajna chakra or "third eye" which is the seat of intuitive power. Eyes may also be closed down 9/10ths and focused at the tip of the nose (this creates a neutral, non-judgmental mind).

MANTRA

Most meditations use special breath rhythms (such as inhaling in sixteen parts and exhaling in sixteen parts) or mantras (sound current). Each *mantra* (ma = mind, tra = vibration) has a specific vibratory effect when done vocally or silently. Mantras are combinations of syllables designed to connect the human being with various states of consciousness. Rhythmical breathing enhances the effect of the meditation.

Mantras chanted in English are powerful and effective; however, there are specific benefits to chanting mantras in a spiritual language, such as Hebrew, Persian, and Sanskrit. When the mind does not have to relate to preconceived notions about the meaning of the words, it is easier to surrender to the power of the chant. Kundalini Yoga mantras are in Gurmukhi, a language based on the ancient yogic science of sound vibration called *Naad*. The vibrations of the mantras, in combination with touching the tongue to the 84 meridian points on the upper palate of the mouth literally change the chemistry of the brain. This creates an experience for many people of heightened awareness, inner serenity, or ecstasy. This must occur in order to gain admittance into the chamber of higher consciousness. For this reason, mantras chanted in the Gurmukhi language are very powerful. An example of a mantra to begin the journey of self-awareness is **ANG SANG WAHE GURU** (pronounced "ung sung waahay g' roo") which means "God is in every part of me." Yogi Bhajan also taught this mantra in English as God and Me, Me and God, Are One.

"Using mantras during sex helps me stay within the flow of energy; it helps me to be with my husband in the moment. Chanting also helps me to let go of old fears and beliefs about sex." – Amber (yoga student)

MEDITATION TO OPEN THE HEART CENTER

If you feel your heart is closed and there is no flow of love, do this meditation. Sit in a comfortable cross-legged position. Focus your eyes up between the eyebrows at the third eye point. The mantra SAAT KAARTAAR, which means "God is the Doer," can be chanted melodically or in a monotone in three parts with a different mudra for each syllable. Transition from step to step in a single flowing movement.

Fig.1

Step 1. As you chant **SAAT**, the palms of the hands are pressed together in prayer mudra at the center of the chest. (Fig. 1)

Fig.2

Step 2. As you chant **KAAR**, extend your arms out in front of you with the hands and fingers pointed straight up, palms facing away from you. (Fig. 2)

Step 3. As you say **TAAR**, extend your arms out from the sides parallel to the floor, with the palms facing up. (Fig. 3)

Fig.3

Time: 5–31 minutes.

DEEP RELAXATION

After completing your meditation, it is time to deeply relax. This will allow the effects of the meditation to assimilate into the body, in order to tune into the internal wisdom of the Self. Following the meditation, lie down and totally relax the body. Lying on the floor, close your eyes and begin long, deep breathing. Tune in to your breath as you inhale and exhale slowly through the nose. As you breathe, become aware of external stimuli. What do you hear going on around you? Perhaps voices, music, the wind in the trees, or cars honking. Just be aware of them. Now turn your attention to odors and fragrances. Next, bring your attention to any sensation on your skin. Then, focus your attention on one sensation and magnify it. Becoming aware of as many sensations as possible at once, equalize them into the same intensity.

The next step is to bring the awareness to your body. Imagine that you are breathing into the bottom of your feet. Become aware of and relax your feet. Proceed to "breathe" up the legs, bringing awareness to your calves, knees and thighs. As you go through the various parts of your body, notice how they feel. Are they tense, relaxed, in pain? If your body feels tense, use your breath to relax the tightness. Continue up your body, allowing the breath to flow into the hips, buttocks, abdomen, stomach, and chest. All the while, bring awareness and breath into each area. Next, breathe into your fingertips, palms, arms and shoulders. Use your imagination to transform the breath into healing energy, which is flowing into all areas of your body. Next, bring your awareness to the lower part of your spine. From the base of the spine, breathe up through each vertebra until you reach the neck. Bring awareness and relaxation to each area of the spine.

Finally, breathe the energy into your head, relaxing each part of the face, including your chin, cheeks, jaw, nose, ears, eyes, forehead, temples, scalp, hair and brain. Each time you inhale, imagine that you are breathing energy and vitality into your body. As you exhale, release tension, discomfort, and disease. On each exhale, feel your body becoming heavier, as though it were sinking into the floor.

In this state of heightened awareness and relaxation, your body will give you messages. Listen to them. This is the first step in getting in touch with inner feelings, such as sensuality, joy, sadness, or spirituality. All these facets are within you. Develop your inner awareness in order to establish a spiritual relationship with your soul, mind and body.

CHAPTER 5

KUNDALINI YOGA AND SEXUALITY

Kundalini Yoga is the science of awareness. "Kundal" means the "coil of the hair of the Beloved." Through this ancient practice, the dormant energy that resides at the base of the spine is raised from the lower energy centers to the crown of the head. This is the seat of spiritual ecstasy and enlightenment. For the practitioner of yoga, sex is a sacred and conscious act of channeling the creative energy forces of the body for healing and experiencing of God consciousness.

"Male and female make a union and this complete union is the greatest yoga." – Yogi Bhajan

Seminal fluid in both the male and female contains high concentrations of minerals and elements crucial to proper nerve balance and brain function. If the seminal fluid is allowed to mature, rather than being ejaculated, it becomes re-absorbed by the body into the spinal fluid. When seminal fluid is weak, the nerves will be shaky and insensitive, and aging will occur more rapidly. The normal span of potency for a yogi can equal the length of his lifespan. In the West, potency for many men wanes even in their early forties.

EXERCISES FOR SEXUALITY

The Kundalini Yoga techniques presented in this chapter include exercises for male potency, sex organ vitality, prolonging ejaculation, and building and raising the prana (life force energy) to the higher chakras (see Chapter 6). Yogic exercises for women also enhance feminine vitality, radiance, and hormonal balance.

GETTING STARTED

As in the meditation section presented in the last chapter, choose a quiet space and wear comfortable clothing. Tune in by chanting **ONG NAMO GURU DEV NAMO** and **AAD GURAY NAMEH, JUGAAD GURAY NAMEH, SAAT GURAY NAMEH, SIREE GURU DAYV-AY NAMEH.**

BREATHING TECHNIQUES

Long Deep Breathing

Long deep breathing techniques are very powerful. Breathing deeply can:

- cleanse the blood
- bring clarity and neutrality to the mind
- calm and revitalize the body
- clear mucous from the lungs
- expand the aura (electromagnetic field around the body)
- stimulate endorphins in the brain
- manage physical and emotional pain
- enhance one's sexual experience

To practice long, deep breathing, lie down on the floor. Place one palm over the lower abdomen, the other arm is resting at your side, with the palm up. Inhale through the nostrils into the lower abdomen. Allow the breath to inflate the lower abdomen like a balloon. As the lower abdomen expands, it will push the palm up. Keep inhaling. The breath will automatically rise upward until it reaches the chest, expanding this area as well. Pause, holding the breath a couple of seconds. Then, exhale through your nose, reversing the process. The chest will lower all the way down to the lower abdomen. Pull the abdomen down.

Breath of Fire

The next basic breathing technique is Breath of Fire, which is the long deep breathing technique done rapidly, except the air does not go up into the chest area. This breath is fairly rapid (two to three breaths per second), continuous and powerful, with no pause between the inhale and exhale. As you exhale, the air is pushed out by pulling the navel point and abdomen in towards the spine. In this motion, the chest area stays moderately relaxed. The focus of the energy is at the navel point. The breath in and out should be equal in volume. At first, you may feel awkward doing Breath of Fire. However, once the muscles are comfortable with the motion, it is very relaxing and energizing. Start by practicing this technique slowly, building up to a rapid pace.

The 4/4 Breath For Energy

When you want a cup of coffee, do this breath technique instead. It will revitalize and energize you physically and mentally in just a few minutes. During sexual intercourse, this breath can be used to subtly enhance feelings of ecstasy and raise the energy to the higher chakras.

To practice 4/4 breath, sit with a straight spine. Put the palms together at the center of the chest, with the fingers pointing up (Prayer Pose) and thumbs pressing against the sternum. A continuous pressure against the palms should be maintained throughout the breathing. Powerfully inhale through the nose in four equal parts (like sniffs) and exhale in four equal parts. The lungs should be completely filled at the end of the fourth inhale and empty at the end of the fourth exhale. On each part of the inhale and exhale, pull in the navel point. The stronger you pump the navel the more energy you will generate. One full breath cycle (in and out) takes about seven to eight seconds. Continue for 2–3 minutes. To maintain mental focus, you can mentally chant **SAA TAA NAA MAA**, one sound for each sniff in and out.

When you are done, inhale and hold the breath, pressing the palms against one another with force for 10–20 seconds. Exhale. Repeat this two more times. Relax. Take a couple of deep breaths, stretch and feel refreshed. During sexual intercourse, this technique can be done subtly, with the sound of the breath going in and out of the nostrils silently.

Circular Visualization

Long deep breathing can be used to channel energy up through the chakras or into any part of the body that needs healing following any Kundalini Yoga posture or meditation, by visualizing energy moving up and down the spine. As the energy travels up through the chakras (see Chapter 6), energy blocks can be opened and cleared. As the energy goes down the front, the energy can be used to heal and revitalize glands and organs.

Begin by inhaling slowly and deeply, directing the energy up the spine, from the base of the spine to the top of the head. You can visualize the energy spiraling around the spine or as a beam of light moving upwards through the center of the spine. This can be done in one deep breath or in several short sniffs through the nose. When the inhale is completed, hold the breath in for a moment. Focus the eyes at the brow point ("third eye") or top of the head. Then, as you exhale, direct the energy down the front of your body, from the third eye down to the navel center. Continue inhaling and exhaling in this way, channeling the energy up the back and down the front in a circular pattern.

KUNDALINI YOGA POSTURES

Inverted Bow Pose for Potency

This exercise is very healthful for both men and women. It stimulates male potency. For women, it is revitalizing for the female organs and can help balance the hormones in the ovaries, regulating the monthly cycle and alleviating cramps.

Lie on your back. Bending the knees with your feet on the ground, grasp the ankles. Inhale and raise the buttocks, pushing the navel point up. Exhale and relax down. Continue for a total of 26 times.

Archer Pose

Archer Pose is a very powerful posture for strengthening the nerves, improving the digestive system and cleansing the body of toxins. It builds male potency. For a woman, this exercise brings energy to the sex nerve, in the inside of the thigh. It strengthens her navel center, building her confidence and strength. When done properly, Archer Pose also affects the 108 minerals of the body, especially the calcium, magnesium and potassium balance, especially important for women.

Stand with the right leg bent forward so the knee is directly over the toes. The left leg is straight back with the foot flat on the ground at a 45-degree angle to the front foot. Raise the right arm straight in front, parallel to the ground. Make a fist as if grasping a bow, with the thumb straight up. Pull your left arm back as if pulling a bowstring back to the shoulder. Create a tension across the chest. Face forward. Fix the eyes above the tip of the thumb to the horizon. Hold the position for 3–5 minutes, then switch legs and arms and repeat.

Sat Kriya

Sat Kriya is one of the most exalted and powerful of all Kundalini Yoga kriyas. This technique massages all the internal organs, stimulates the release of navel energy, stimulates the third chakra, opens the spine to an easy flow of prana and spinal fluid, and implants the *bij* mantra **SAAT NAAM** in the subconscious. Many illnesses come from a lack of coordination or timing between the glands or organs. The navel point stimulation and rhythmic breathing and motion in Sat Kriya coordinates the timing of your entire system. It increases sexual potency while transforming excess sexual energy into creative expressions through the higher chakras.

To practice Sat Kriya, sit on the heels in Rock Pose, with the arms straight up hugging both sides of the head. Either interlace the fingers with the index fingers pointing up and touching each other along their length or have the palms together with the fingers straight and pressed together. The spine should be straight, with the chin tucked in about one inch down and one inch back.

Begin chanting the mantra **SAAT NAAM** (which translates as "Truth is my Name"). As **SAAT** is chanted, pull up on the the rectum, sex organs and diaphragm. As **NAAM** is chanted, release. This mantra should be chanted and vibrated powerfully from the navel point for 1-3 minutes. Then inhale and hold the breath while squeezing up on the muscles of the anus, sex organs, and navel point. Visualize energy flowing up from the base of the spine through the top of the skull. Exhale. Inhale again, exhale, and relax on your back with your arms along your sides, palms facing up, for at least as long as you practiced Sat Kriya.

Leg Lift for Potency

This exercise is for male and female potency. It works on the life nerve, which runs along the back of the legs, from the buttocks to the heels. Lie down on your back. Bring your legs to a 90-degree angle. Hold onto your toes. Breathe normally. This exercise can also be done with a special breath, in which the tongue slightly protrudes out and is rolled lengthwise. The inhale is through the curled tongue, the exhale is through the nose. This breath cools and relaxes the entire body.

Asana to Vitalize the Sex Organs

Squat with the feet flat on the ground, back parallel to the floor and head facing forward. Wrap your arms around the inside of your thighs with your hands holding the ankles from the outside. Do Breath of Fire for 3 minutes. Relax.

Male Potency Exercise

On hands and knees, raise the right hand off the ground, bending the arm, and raise the left leg parallel to the ground. Deeply inhale, hold the breath and lift the leg high up in the air, and back to parallel, eight times, with the knee remaining straight. Then exhale, bringing the leg parallel. Inhale and and repeat the series for a maximum of 11 minutes. Switch sides and repeat.

Potency Bounce

Sit with the soles of the feet touching. Put your hands in front of you on the ground, and shift your weight forward until balanced on the sides of your feet and hands. The buttocks are off the ground. Begin bouncing the buttocks up and down (buttocks may touch the sides of feet) while thinking of sex and feeling horny. Continue for 1–11 minutes.

WOMAN'S DAILY EXERCISES FOR BEAUTY, RADIANCE, AND GRACE

It is extremely beneficial for every woman to exercise daily. Kundalini Yoga improves the circulation and strengthens the nervous and glandular systems, bringing a natural beauty, radiance, and grace. The following exercise series can be done regularly to keep the spine, internal organs, and nervous system strong and vital. Follow this series with deep relaxation. Yoga can also help reverse the aging process, which enhances the sex drive and overall sense of well-being.

ROCK POSE: Sit on your heels with palms resting on the thighs or relax the hands on the lap, spine straight and relaxed. With long, deep breathing, meditate at the brow point for 2 minutes.

LIFE NERVE STRETCH: Sit on your right heel with your left leg extended straight out and draw your forehead to the left knee, with long, deep breathing, holding onto the ankle of the extended leg for 1–3 minutes. Change sides and repeat. Variation: Extend both legs straight out in front and proceed as above for 1–3 minutes. This posture stretches the life nerve, which runs along the back of the leg.

CAMEL POSE: Kneel and arch the back up, pressing the pelvis forward, dropping the head back, hands grasping the heels, with long, deep breathing or breath of fire for 2–3 minutes. This adjusts the reproductive organs.

SHOULDER STAND: On your back, raise the legs and then torso (forming a straight line from shoulders to toes), supporting the back with the hands, weight on neck, shoulders and elbows, chin pressed into chest for 2–3 minutes. This stimulates the thyroid gland and releases pressure on 11 internal organs.

ARCHER POSE: Stand with the right leg bent forward so the toes can't be seen over the knee. The left leg is straight back with the foot flat on the ground at a 45-degree angle to the front foot. Raise the right arm straight in front, parallel to the ground. Make a fist as if grasping a bow, with the thumb straight up. Pull your left arm back as if pulling a bowstring back to the shoulder. Create a tension across the chest. Face forward. Fix the eyes at the tip of the thumb to the horizon. Hold the position for 2–3 minutes, then switch legs and arms and repeat.

BABY POSE: Sitting on the heels, bring your forehead to the floor, arms behind, relaxed at sides, palms up, with long deep breathing for 1–2 minutes. Good for digestion and releasing gas.

BOW POSE: On your stomach, grasp the ankles, and pull the hands and feet up, raising the thighs, head and feet up, as high as possible. Hold with long, deep breathing for 2–3 minutes.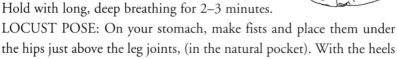

LOCUST POSE: On your stomach, make fists and place them under the hips just above the leg joints, (in the natural pocket). With the heels together and the chin on floor, deeply inhale, raise the legs and hold with long, deep breathing for 2–3 minutes. This exercise balances the hormones in the ovaries.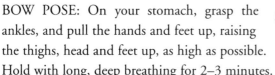

COW POSE: To balance the hormones in the thyroid gland, on your hands and knees, raise the head, allowing the spine to relax down, the arms are straight and parallel to thighs, and hold with long, deep breathing for 2–3 minutes.

CAT POSE: On your hands and knees as above, allow your head to fall forward, chin to chest, and arch the spine up and hold with long, deep breathing for 2–3 minutes.

STRETCH POSE: On your back, raise the head, heels and hands six inches from the floor. The heels are together, with the eyes staring at the toes. Extend the arms so that the hands are a few inches above the thighs with the fingers pointing toward the toes. Hold this position with Breath of Fire for 3 minutes. This exercise strengthens the navel center.

 CORPSE POSE: Relax on your back, arms at sides, palms up for 1 minute.

SAT KRIYA: To practice Sat Kriya, sit on the heels in Rock Pose, with the arms straight up hugging both sides of the head. Either interlace the fingers with the index fingers pointing up and touching each other along their length or have the palms together with the fingers straight and pressed together. The spine should be straight, with the chin tucked in about one inch down and one inch back.

Begin chanting the mantra **SAT NAM** (which translates as "Truth is my Name"). As **SAT** is chanted, pull up on the the rectum, sex organs and diaphragm. As **NAM** is chanted, release. This mantra should be chanted and vibrated powerfully from the navel point for 1-3 minutes. Then inhale and hold the breath while squeezing up on the muscles of the anus, sex organs, and navel point. Visualize energy flowing up from the base of the spine through the top of the skull. Exhale. Inhale again, exhale, and relax on your back with your arms along your sides, palms facing up, for at least as long as you practiced Sat Kriya.

SEXUAL NERVE STRENGTH

This Kundalini Yoga set stimulates the flow of sexual energy, allowing the energy to circulate freely. According to Yogi Bhajan, it is good to create a habit of practicing a kriya like this frequently. If you do it while you are young, your body will not fail you when you are older.

Exercise 1. Lie on the back with the legs straight up in the air. Lift the buttocks up in the air in shoulder stand, supported by the hands. Begin to kick the buttocks with alternating heels. Continue for 3 minutes. Then, rest the buttocks down on the floor and again begin the kicking motion. Continue for 3 minutes, then relax for 2 minutes. Now repeat the series, breathing long and deep in the second part. This simulates the nerve reflex area in the buttocks.

Exercise 2. Sit on the heels (Rock Pose). Have the hands in Venus Lock (fingers interlaced with the left thumb in the web of the right thumb for women and right thumb in the web of the left thumb for men). Place this mudra in your lap and meditate for 2 minutes. This exercise helps improve the digestion. It is an excellent pose for women to practice daily.

Exercise 3. Lie on your back. Slowly lift your legs to a 90-degree angle as you slowly inhale and pull the muscles of the sex organs. Slowly exhale as you lower the legs and release the muscle tension at the sex organ. Keep the contraction constant. Repeat between 4 and 10 times. This exercise gives endurance and integrates the release of sexual energy into the other body systems. Relax completely on your back.

The Art of Making Sex Sacred

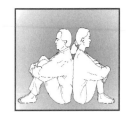

CHAKRAS AND ENERGY

The art of sacred sex requires us to engage all our senses. Indeed, sensuality is as great a part of the experience of sexuality as is the physical act of arousal and consummation. When the whole person is involved, the soul can then truly unfold itself, like a lotus of countless petals. Awakening the many-petalled lotus through Kundalini Yoga allows a couple to enjoy a heightened experience of consciousness before, during, and after making love. This can lead to the ultimate merging into oneness that transcends the individual bonds of relationships.

THE EIGHT CHAKRAS

The human body has energy centers, including the seven *chakras,* the *arcline,* and the electromagnetic field or *aura,* which are fountains of spiritual energy, invisible to the human eye. These energy centers can be awakened through Kundalini Yoga or other forms of practice which utilize breath techniques, visualization, or physical exercise to awaken the dormant energies along the spine. The chakras also symbolize or manifest an aspect of a person's consciousness, or mode of behavior. In a sense, chakras function as an "etheric counterpart" of an important nerve center or gland. Thus, when our spirit is not in harmony

"Sex is not what you think sex is. Sex is your creative power installed in you by nature. It can go to the extent of being sexual, being horny, which we already know, but also the same sex when it rises only 36 inches to the third eye, can totally enable you to know what is going on."–Yogi Bhajan

with our true nature, the symptoms often manifest in either neurotic behavior or physical ailments.

A person who manifests harmony and balance with their mental, spiritual and physical selves will experience a flow of energy between all the energy centers, resulting in a greater feeling of well-being and connection. Where there is an energy blockage (caused by fear or a physical symptom of an emotional or spiritual block), the flow of energy to the higher centers will be impeded. A person's behavior may be especially destructive if the blockage is in the lower three chakras, which aligns with our survival needs and often manifests in sexual abuse or dysfunction.

All the chakras are equally vital. The lower chakras are the foundation on which the higher centers are built. It is important to understand their purpose in order to maximize one's sexual and spiritual potential. Each chakra has a specific color frequency, correlates to a specific organ or system of the body, and manifests certain qualities or behaviors in a person when activated.

The Chakras

The **First Chakra** (Muladara) is located at the rectum. Its energy frequency relates to the color red, and its quality is the element Earth. The first center relates to elimination, instinct, survival, and habits. Blockages and improper functioning of the first chakra are often associated with tendencies of destructive sexual behavior. Also associated with blockages in this chakra are extreme attachments to material objects. A person "stuck" in this energy center might have a lot of material possessions and manifest obsessive concerns about them or exhibits a "poverty consciousness" and expends much time and energy involved with survival issues. When energy is blocked at this first center, there might also be a tendency to be stubborn, overly clinging, addictive, and ungrounded or spacey.

When the first chakra functions properly, a person is well-grounded, dependable, realistic, secure and comfortable with his or her existence on the earth plane.

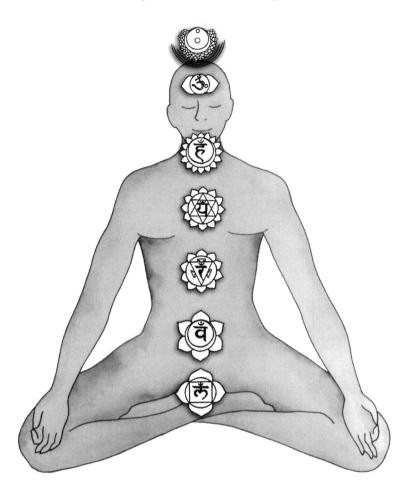

The **Second Chakra** (Svadhishthama) is located at the sex organs. Its frequency corresponds to the color orange, and its quality is that of Water. Blockages and improper functioning cause a person to be preoccupied with sex. The person's activities probably would not be illegal or pathological, but he or she would be neurotically obsessed with sex, or overly puritanical. A balanced second chakra allows people to be expressive, balanced in their relationships and have a sense of their individuality. They will pursue their creative capacities in many other areas besides reproduction or sexual endeavors. The second chakra is the seat of creative energy.

The **Third Chakra** (Manipura) resides in the navel point/solar plexus area. The adrenal glands help maintain a strong navel point chakra. Its frequency corresponds to saffron-yellow, and its quality is that of Fire. It is the center of physical well-being and a source of energy and cleansing. If it is even slightly misaligned, the body becomes susceptible to illness. A weak navel center leads to weakness of character, lack of nerve strength and premature aging.

The navel center must be developed, however, in balance with the other chakras. A well-developed navel center that is blocked from transmitting the energy to the heart chakra will lead to greed, ego gratification, quest for power, and possessive sexual relations. An open navel center leads one to use his or her abilities to help others and to take society into consideration when determining one's actions.

The first three centers or "the lower triangle," relate to the mind, and habit patterns. Much of our society today is dominated by behavior resulting from the imbalance of the lower three chakras.

The higher centers relate to the spirit and our higher potential. The energy of the lower centers gives us a base or framework for the experience of the higher ones.

The **Fourth Chakra** (Anahata) is the heart center (thymus gland) at the area of the sternum. Its frequency corresponds to the color green and its quality is that of Air. The heart center is the first center of higher consciousness. It is the seat of compassion and caring. It relates to love, expansion and the tenacity of the human spirit. When the heart center is open it is possible to experience one's Infinite identity, selfless sacrifice and unconditional love.

An underdeveloped heart center leads to egotistical motivations and emotional reactions in personal relationships. Such behavior would include someone manipulating a love relationship for his or her gain. The person may be hardhearted and lack compassion, or he or she may not be able to set clear boundaries and know when to say "no."

The **Fifth Chakra** (Vishudha) resides at the throat center, which relates to the thyroid gland. Its frequency corresponds to the color light blue and its quality is Ether. It is the seat of spoken expression and creativity. When the energy is flowing through the throat center, one is able to speak and live the Truth, directly and assertively. When the throat center is blocked the person feels creatively stifled and may face challenges in being direct and truthful with others.

The **Sixth Chakra** (Ajna) is at the "third eye," or a point midway between the eyebrows, one half inch up and one half inch below the surface. Its frequency relates to the color indigo and its quality is so subtle it cannot be defined. The pituitary gland is here and it is the doorway to intuitive awareness and knowledge.

According to Yogi Bhajan, without opening the third eye, one is forced to calculate and think through all of one's actions and the consequences. When the third eye is opened, one becomes intuitively aware of what to do and not to do, what is right or wrong. Duality is gradually reduced and eliminated. A person becomes more relaxed and at peace because he knows where he is going and how to get there.

The **Seventh Chakra** (Sahastrara) reveals the thousand-petalled lotus, or the seat of the soul. Its frequency corresponds to the color violet. It is the seat of the pineal gland. It is the gateway to discovery of ourselves and our relationship to the rest of the universe. It is the seat of universal consciousness. A dormant pineal gland will keep us in ignorance of the higher aspects of ourselves and the universe about us.

The **Eighth Center** is the aura and represents the working balance of all the centers. It is our shield, protection and projection. While it guards us against negativity and illness, it also attracts opportunities and positivity to us. If it is weak or damaged, the opposite can occur.

When we develop our flow of Kundalini energy, we can raise it up to the higher centers of spiritual enlightenment. We have a choice in how to use this atomic sexual energy. We can use it for sexual intimacy and ecstasy, or we can use it for healing and awakening our beings. There are many disciplines which teach how to tap into the body's energy and direct it up through the chakras. Kundalini Yoga is one effective way to keep the chakras open and in balance.

KUNDALINI YOGA TO CLEAR THE CHAKRAS

The following is a simple and effective yoga set to open and balance the chakras and remove energy blocks. Follow each exercise with Circular Visualization to the chakra activated; spiral the energy around each chakra to energize the chakra. Before and after each exercise, you can lightly massage each center to help release energy. Do each exercise 1–3 minutes. To end the exercise, inhale, hold the breath, and relax.

EASY POSE. Pull the muscles of the anus, sex organs and navel point (Root Lock). Center yourself and stimulate energy with the breath of fire or long deep breathing. (**First, Second, Third Chakras**)

PELVIC ROTATIONS. Grind the waist in circles on the pelvis, coordinating the breath with the movement. To end, inhale long and deep. Using the breath and visualization, bring the energy from below the navel and sex organ to the base of the spine and coccyx. Hold, feel the energy. Exhale, relax the breath and come back to center. Repeat one or more times. (**First, Second, Third Chakras**)

SPINAL FLEXES. Sit in a comfortable cross-legged position. Place the hands on the ankles. Inhale and flex the spine flexes forward, pushing out the chest. Exhale and flex the spine back, collapsing the chest. Continue to flex the spine, emphasizing the lower back. To end, inhale long and deep. Use the breath and visualization to bring the energy from below the navel and sex organ up the base of the spine to the sacrum. Hold, feel the energy. Exhale, relax the breath and come back to center. Repeat, and then relax. (**First, Second, Third Chakras**)

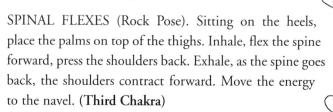

SPINAL FLEXES (Rock Pose). Sitting on the heels, place the palms on top of the thighs. Inhale, flex the spine forward, press the shoulders back. Exhale, as the spine goes back, the shoulders contract forward. Move the energy to the navel. (**Third Chakra**)

SIDE TWISTS. Place the hands on the shoulders, fingers in front, thumbs in back. Inhale, twist from the waist to the left, exhale, twist right. Move the energy to the heart center. (**Fourth Chakra**)

SHOULDER SHRUGS. Inhale, press the shoulders up, exhale, let them drop down. Move the energy to the throat. Maximum 2 minutes. (**Fifth Chakra**)

NECK ROLLS. Exhale, let the head drop down. Inhale, rotate the head to the left and back, exhale, to the right and down. Move the energy to the base of the skull.(**Sixth Chakra**)

COW POSE. On the hands and knees, the lower spine arches down, the head is arched back. Move the energy to the third eye. Do Breath of Fire. (**Sixth Chakra**)

CAT-COW. Inhale into Cow Pose. Exhale into Cat Pose. The head lowers, chin toward the chest, the spine arches up. The arms and legs remain stationary, like pillars. Move the energy to the center of the head. (**Seventh Chakra**)

SHAKTI POSE. Sitting in Easy Pose, place the hands over the head in Venus Lock (fingers are interlaced). Do Breath of Fire. Move the energy to the top of the head and around. Then practice moving the energy out the top of the head into the cosmos and back. (**Seventh Chakra**)

ENERGY AND THE BODY

Every society in history has its own philosophy about how energy is used in the body. It was called Ki by the Japanese, Chi by the Chinese, Ruach by the Hebrew prophets, Ruh by the Sufi saints, Pneuma by the Greeks, and Prana by the Indian yogis.

If we understand energy and recognize how it flows in our bodies, we can improve the quality of our lives. One of the main complaints we have in our fast, stress-filled lives is that we don't have enough energy. We try to find more energy in a pill or stimulants like coffee, cola or chocolate, which only create havoc in our nervous system. Is it any wonder we are often too tired for sex? But there is a more effective way to tap our natural energy flows.

Pranic energy and the Kundalini are essential ingredients in the practice of sacred sexuality.

PRANIC ENERGY

In its purest, divine form, prana is the basic life energy. It is the life force of the atom we bring into the body with every breath we take. Apana is elimination or the eliminative force which is in the outgoing breath. To carry the pranic energy, there are three main nerve currents in the body, known as the Ida, Pingala and Shushmana. The Ida and Pingala are subtle tubes which make two and one-half turns around the the Shushmana, the central column of the spine, as they spiral upwards from the base of the spine, ending in the nostrils. The Ida ends in the left nostril, the Pingala ends in the right nostril. They carry the vital pranic energy into the body each time we breathe through the nostrils. The left side, the Ida, is the moon, feminine, cooling energy. The right side, the Pingala, corresponds to the sun, masculine, hot energy.

Prana is difficult to describe because we cannot see it. However, we can feel it. In the physical realm, it is the air we breathe, which revitalizes us and keeps us alive. We transform this raw air by mixing it with other nutrients, refining it into solid forms like blood, bones, and flesh. The energy is further refined, producing our thoughts, dreams, and emotions, as it continuously pulsates and flows through each cell. Its rhythm is so natural we hardly notice it.

Ancient Eastern masters, Taoists, yogis, monks, spent a great deal of time observing and studying this pranic or chi force, which is the breath of the universe, flowing through everything.

POLARITY ENERGIES

"Heaven is lasting and Earth enduring. The reason for this is that they do not live for themselves alone; therefore they live long." – Tao Te Ching

Pranic energy can be described as polarity energies in the universe. The mystical teachings of the East recognize the forces of Heaven and Earth as the two fundamental principles that pervade everything. Tibetan Buddhists call them Yah (father) and Yum (mother). Hindus refer to them as Shiva and Shakti, and Taoists see them as Yang and Yin. These two forces are seen and experienced in many forms – light and dark, positive and negative, hot and cold, wet and dry, solid and fluid, male and female.

All of us have both energies, Yin and Yang, within us. Yin energy is more intuitive, flowing, receptive. Yang is aggressive, the doer. Yin intuitively tells us what's right, Yang, gives us the power to manifest the rightness into reality. In these times, more people are allowing themselves to experience the power and beauty of both of these energies within themselves. Men, being predominately Yang, manifest the action qualities, while women, being predominately Yin, manifest the nurturing ones. Nevertheless, as we break out of our gender roles, we can be aware of both energies existing in each of us. They can harmoniously serve us to live more fulfilled and balanced lives. The pranic energy embodies everything in the universe, in either Yang or Yin form. Now we shall explore how this energy is transformed into Kundalini energy.

THE KUNDALINI

A quote by Vivekananda, in *To Know God,* sums up the power of Kundalini energy and its importance to spirituality. He states: *"Whenever there is a manifestation of what is ordinarily called supernatural power or wisdom, a little current of Kundalini must have found its way into the Shushumna. Whenever there is divinity in you, the Kundalini Power must have touched the central nerve. Only, in the vast majority of such cases, people have stumbled on some practice, which set free a minute portion of the coiled up Kundalini. All worship, conscious or unconscious, leads to this end. The man who thinks he is receiving a response to his prayer, does not know that the fulfillment comes from his own nature, that he has succeeded by the mental attitude of prayer, in awakening a bit of Infinite Power which is coiled up within himself."*

The third nerve current in the body is called the Shushumna which runs through the center of the spinal column. The aim of the yogis is to move the Kundalini or "creative" energy up through the Shushumna nerve current. This current starts from the rectum and goes up to the top of the head. Dormant Kundalini energy is stored at the fourth vertebra of the spinal column. Kundalini has been described in yogic mythology as a serpent coiled 3 1/2 times. In order for *samadhi,* or bliss, to be experienced, the Kundalini must be awakened.

In the practice of pranayama (breath techniques), yoga positions and meditation, the prana and apana energies mix at the navel center, producing heat and thereby raising the Kundalini up the Shushumna. The Kundalini then begins its journey through the chakras, beginning at the rectum until it reaches the top of the head. Symbolically the Kundalini hisses like a serpent beaten with a stick and enters the hole of the Sushumna. When it travels from chakra to chakra, layer after layer of the mind opens, and one experiences an elevation of consciousness. The application of Kundalini Yoga practice to sexuality brings about the full realization of our infinite creative powers to heal, manifest prosperity and merge in blissful, bountiful relationships with ourselves and others.

RAISING THE KUNDALINI

The technique used by yogis to raise the Kundalini energy is the application of *Bandhs* or locks, practiced during Kundalini Yoga exercises and meditation. All of these locks should be practiced while sitting with a straight spine. They are essential in the practice of Kundalini Yoga for raising the energy up the spine through the chakras.

Jalandhara Bandh or Neck Lock is the most basic lock used in Kundalini Yoga. The chin and throat are contracted together. The chin is pressed in (not down) like a soldier.

Uddiyana Bandh or Diaphragm Lock is applied by lifting the diaphragm up high into the thorax and pulling the upper abdominal organs back toward the spine. It is normally only applied on the exhale.

Mul Bandh or Root Lock is a method to close off the lower three chakras, allowing the Kundalini to rise up the spine. Inhale and exhale deeply a few times, still holding the chest high. While the breath is held either in or out, first contract or squeeze the muscles of the rectum (anal sphincter), the sex organs, and the navel. It is very important that the spine is very straight, enabling the Kundalini Energy to travel upward. Mul Bandh is especially effective during sexual arousal to enhance ecstasy and to prolong ejaculation and can be used with the 4/4 breath technique (see. p. 33). If it is practiced on a regular basis, one will feel comfortable and natural using it during sex.

Maha Bandh or Great Lock is the application of all three of the above locks simultaneously. When all of the locks are applied, the nerves and glands are rejuvenated. Normally the breath is held out.

53

Practicing the Locks

1. Sit on the heels with the knees spread apart. The palms are on the thighs. Holding the breath either in or out, apply the root lock and then relax it.

2. Hold the breath out, and apply the diaphragm lock and relax it.

3. While holding the breath either in or out, apply the neck lock and relax it.

4. While the breath is held out, apply all three locks at once.

Repeat this in a continuous series for 3–11 minutes.

CHAPTER 7

VENUS KRIYAS FOR COUPLES

The ancient yogis understood that a worship-ful attitude creates a neuro-chemical change in the brain. This allows the experience of ecstasy and bliss. In this chapter we present sacred yogic med-itations for couples, called *Shukra* (or Venus) *Kriyas,* as a way to amalgamate the experience of oneness for practitioners of Sacred Sex.

VENUS KRIYAS

Venus Kriyas and other meditations for cou-ples are an excellent preparation for lovemaking or as a regular spiritual practice. It is especially effec-tive if couples choose one meditation that they practice consistently for 40, 90, or 120 days to enhance a particular aspect of their relationship. These couples meditations are a very beautiful practice, which can elevate the relationship to a higher level.

Venus Kriyas are very powerful yogic tech-niques. They must be practiced only in the highest consciousness. Venus Kriyas are a tool to blend polarity energies for spiritual growth. The focus stays at the heart, projecting love and caring, with the highest good for both. These practices expand the higher centers. As such, they must never be used for sensual or sexual manipulation or exploitation of another person. If these techniques

"If the feelings are aroused to the point of worship, and the Shakti (female) wor-ships the Shiva (male) and Shiva melts like that of all the early nectar onto her, then it is a unity. But when it is not done as a worship, when she does not perceive and receive him in divinity within herself, [when] he does not go in her as nectar of life and divinity just to give to her, then it is not that act. It only feeds the monstrous ego, and egos clash." – Yogi Bhajan are abused in any way, the result may be harmful to both partners.

GETTING STARTED

First, sit down opposite your partner, put your own hands together in prayer pose and tune in by chanting **ONG NAMO GURU DEV NAMO** followed by **AAD GURAY NAMEH JUGAAD GURAY NAMEH SAT GURAY NAMEH SIREE GURU DAYV-AY NAMEH** three times.

With your hands still together, look into your partner's eyes and bow your head in recognition of their God consciousness. Project love from your heart, and any other positive thought you want, such as, "We deserve all the universe can offer us," or "This lovemaking will be a blissful, spiritual experience for both of us."

When practicing a Venus Kriya, the specified time should be strictly adhered to and only one kriya should be practiced within a six-hour period. Upon completion of the kriya, put your palms together at the heart center and thank your partner. You can then massage each other, and relax completely.

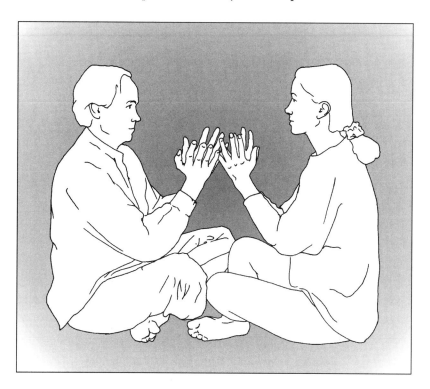

HEART LOTUS

Sit in Easy Pose or Lotus Pose across from your partner, looking into his or her eyes. Form your hands into a lotus: all the fingers are spread with the hands cupped. Then the man puts his little fingers under the woman's little fingers. These are the only fingers that touch. This makes a heart lotus (Fig.1).

Look into the soul, the heart of your partner, through the eyes. Continue for 1-1/2 minutes.

Now place one hand over the other at your heart center. Close your eyes and meditate on your heart. Go deep within, to the center of your being. Continue for 1-1/2 minutes.

To end, inhale deeply and exhale deeply 3 times, then relax.

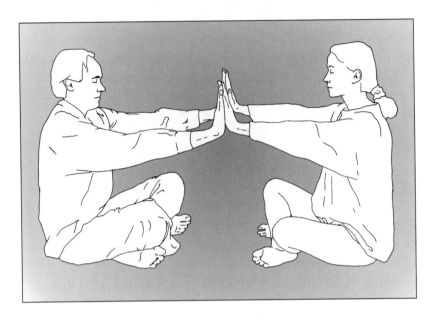

LIFE CURRENT KRIYA

Sit in easy pose with your arms out at shoulder level, touching palms with your partner. Close your eyes and concentrate on your arms, feeling that there is one life current going through you both.

Hold this position for 30 seconds.

Then, inhale and exhale deeply 4 times.

Put your own palms together in prayer pose at your chin and meditate on your own personality, charm, beauty, and God-given life's purpose. You are a Divine being. Meditate on this thought for 2-1/2 minutes, then inhale and exhale.

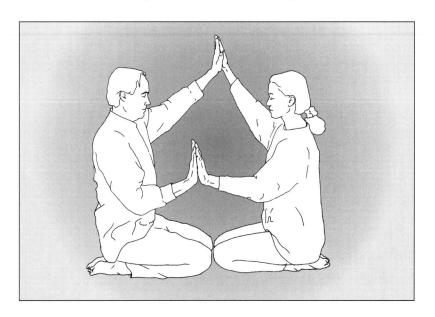

WASHING WINDOWS

Sit on heels in Rock Pose, palms and knees touching those of your partner. Move your hands as if you were washing windows. Do Breath of Fire for 3 minutes.

To end, inhale, hold the breath in, and press hard on the hands. Exhale and relax.

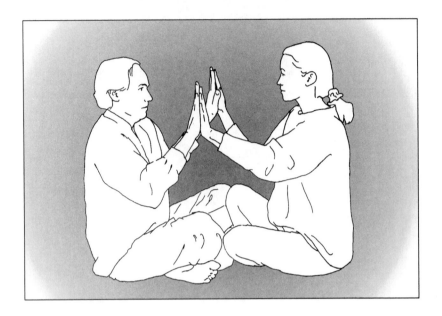

PUSHING PALMS

Sit facing your partner locking into his or her eyes. Put your palms together with your partner's palms at heart level. Knees must be touching. See the Divine in each other.

The mantra is **SAA TAA NAA MAA**. Begin to push the palms back and forth. Chant **SAA** as the right palms go forward, and the left palms go back. Chant **TAA** as the left palms go forward and the right palms go back. Continue in this rhythm with **NAA** and **MAA**.

Continue for 3 minutes.

To end, inhale, exhale and relax.

SENDING PRANA

Sit on your heels in Rock Pose with your arms out at shoulder level, touching palms with your partner. Stare into each other's eyes without blinking. Send prana through the hands and eyes. See your Self in your partner' s eyes.

Continue for 2 minutes.

Then close your eyes and visualize your partner for 1 minute.

To end, inhale, exhale and relax.

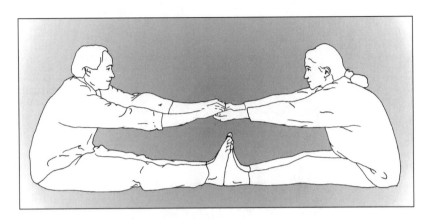

VENUS LIFE NERVE STRETCHES

Sit with legs outstretched in front of you, feet touching your partner's feet. Extend your arms between your outstretched legs and grasp your partner's hands. Curl your fingers into your partner's fingers (Bear Grip).

Look into your partner's eyes, projecting Divine Love.

Continue with normal breathing for 1 minute, then with Breath of Fire for 1-3 minutes.

To end, inhale and hold the breath in, allowing the energy to circulate. Then exhale and apply Mul Bandh (Root Lock).

VENUS LOTUS

Clasp hands with your partner, feet touching your partner's feet. Keeping the feet touching, bend the legs, and bring them up to 60-degree angle from the ground with the arms on the inside of the legs.

Do with either Breath of Fire or long deep breathing for 3 minutes.

Look into each other's eyes, projecting love and Divine Light. See yourself in the other person. Lift the other's vibration. Realize that you two are One.

To end, inhale, exhale and relax.

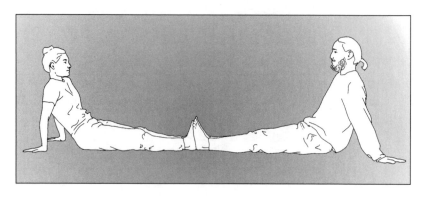

EASY 60-DEGREE LEAN

Stretch your legs out on the ground in front of you, soles of your feet touching those of your partner. Lean back on your hands at a 60-degree angle and begin Breath of Fire.

Continue for 3 minutes. Then inhale, exhale, and relax.

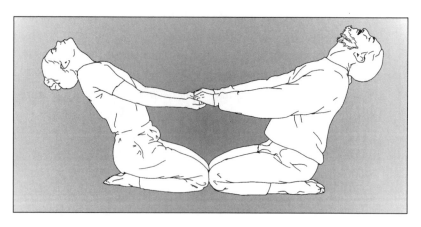

DOUBLE BACK-BEND

Sit on your heels in Rock Pose with your knees touching your partner's knees and clasp hands. Both partners then lean back as far as possible. Breath technique is optional.

Continue for 3 minutes, then inhale, exhale, and relax.

A more difficult variation is Double Back-Stretch.

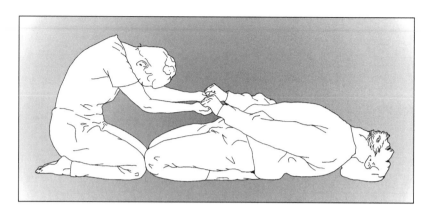

DOUBLE BACK-STRETCH

This kriya is for the heart. It will give you a moderately good physical workout.

Sit on your heels in Rock Pose with your knees touching your partner's knees and clasp hands. Fix your gaze on your partner's eyes, projecting Divine Love.

The woman inhales and leans back, touching her head to the ground as the man exhales and leans forward. Then the woman exhales and leans forward as the man inhales and leans back.

Continue for 1–3 minutes. To end, inhale, exhale, and relax.

VENUS BACK-ROLLS

Sit down back to back with your partner. Exhale and bow forward and down as your partner leans back and down onto your bowed back.

Then inhale and lean back onto your partner's back as your partner bows down. The vertebrae should relate to each other like teeth of a wheel.

Continue for 3 minutes. To end, inhale, exhale and relax.

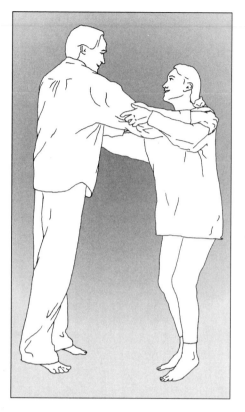

LIVER TWIST

This exercise strengthens the liver. Stand up facing each other. Put your hands on your partner's triceps.

Stand on tiptoes and lean against each other. Begin twisting left and right. You twist one way as you partner twists the other.

Continue for 3 minutes. Then inhale, exhale, and relax.

SHIVA-SHAKTI POSE

Stand facing your partner in Shiva-Shakti Pose. The man's left hand holds the woman's left hand and both right hands are held up. Right upper arms are parallel to the ground.

Look into each other's eyes throughout. Lift up your left leg and balance on your right leg. Your left leg doesn't touch your right leg. Partner's knees do not touch. Holding this position, let yourself become the god Shiva (man) or the goddess Shakti (woman). Let your souls dance. Hold for 3 minutes, changing legs if necessary. Then inhale, exhale and relax.

STRENUOUS CROW

Stand facing your partner. Join hands and look into each other's eyes, projecting Divine Love.

Verbally greet each other. Then squat down together into crow pose, keeping the feet flat on the floor and touching the buttocks to the floor. Stand up and repeat.

Talk to each other throughout the exercise. Each cycle of the exercise should take 3–4 seconds. Continue for 3 minutes.

To end, inhale, exhale and relax.

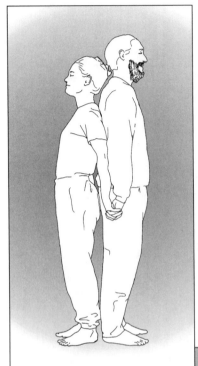

ONE UNIT

Standing back to back with your partner, clasp hands and touch the back of the heads in a relaxed manner (Fig. 1).

Meditate on being one unit and Infinite consciousness.

Normal breathing for 2 minutes. Then drop hands, separate and bend over, keep the buttocks touching, the legs are straight. Touch the ground with the hands for 1 minute (Fig.2).

To end, inhale, exhale and relax.

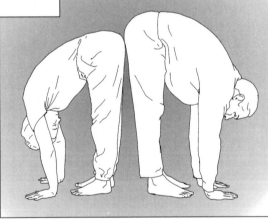

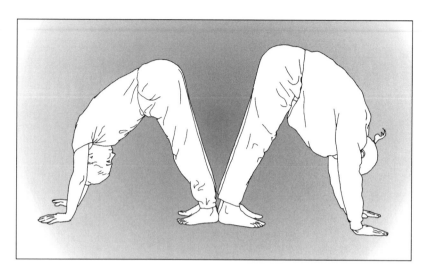

VENUS TRIANGLE

This kriya is for eliminating anger or ending an argument. It helps establish partners as one unit.

Stand back to back, two feet apart from your partner. Feet are hip width apart. Both partners bend over, touching palms to the floor, shoulder width apart and about two feet in front of feet.

Assume triangle pose by meeting partner's' heels with your own, straightening out torso and legs to form a straight line in each direction from the buttocks.

Between the legs, gaze into each other's eyes. Hold the position with Breath of Fire or long deep breathing.

Continue for 3 minutes.

HEART SAVER

Sit in easy pose with a perfectly straight spine. Elbows are even with and upper arms parallel to chin. Forearms are pointing up perpendicular to the ground and touching each other in a straight line from elbows to fingertips. Palms are facing in.

Look at the third eye point. Begin chanting the Guru Gayatri mantra: **GOBINDAY, MUKUNDAY, UDAARAY, APAARAY, HAREEANG, KAREEANG, NIRNAAMAY, AKAAMAY.** (These words describe the eight aspects of God: Sustainer, Liberator, Enlightener, Infinite, Destroyer, Creator, Nameless, Desireless.) You may alternate chanting with your partner or chant in unison. Continue for 3 minutes.

To end, inhale, exhale and relax.

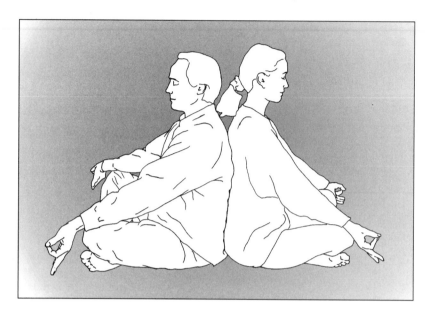

KIRTAN KRIYA TO CLEAR THE CLOUDS

Sit in easy pose back to back with your partner. Hands are in Gyan mudra at the knees. Meditate at the third eye point.

The mantra is **SAA TAA NAA MAA.** As you chant **SAA**, touch the forefinger to the thumb.  On **TAA**, touch the middle finger to the thumb. On **NAA**, touch the ring finger to the thumb. On **MAA**, touch the little finger to the thumb. As you chant each syllable, visualize energy entering the top of the head and pursuing an "L"-shaped course from the top of the head out through the third-eye point, projecting out to Infinity. This energy flows along the energy path called the golden cord, connecting the pineal and the pituitary glands. Begin chanting in a normal voice for 5 minutes. Then whisper for 5 minutes. (Times may be reduced in equal proportion by half for a shorter meditation.) Vibrate the mantra silently for 10 minutes. And finally, chant aloud for 5 minutes. When you have finished, stretch the hands up as far as possible and spread the fingers wide. Stretch the spine and take several deep breaths. Then relax.

MEDITATION TO END AN ARGUMENT

"By being in conflict we are damaging our own psychic power."–Yogi Bhajan

There are always times in a marriage when husband and wife are not in an infinite and graceful consciousness. They want to yell and argue. They have lost the ability to listen, be silent, and act as a single unit of energy. When you have argued and talked until you can talk and argue no longer, do this meditation together. It will break the spell of intolerance and confusion and disperse any latent anger. Ending an argument this way will maintain peace in the subconscious realms so you do not carry the dispute into unrelated areas and times of your relationship.

Sit four to five feet across from your partner, in easy pose with a straight spine. Make fists of both hands. Put both fists with back of hands towards you, six to eight inches in front of the third eye point. Extend and press the thumb tips together firmly until they become very white. Be sure to let the last joint of the thumb relax and bend as much as possible.

Eyes are closed. The mantra is **WHAA HE ("hay") GURU**. With deep, powerful breaths, each partner alternates saying the mantra. Make the pitch as high as possible. You should feel the vibration at the nose and third eye point when you say **GURU** (Guroo). The sound **WHAA HE** lasts about 1 second and the sound **GURU** about 7 seconds. Listen to each other's sound. If the sound is correct, it will penetrate the skull and seem to be inside you. It is essential to keep the eyelids closed. If they are open, you will get faint and dizzy in a few strokes of the chant. If your eyes are closed, you are protected and the effects on consciousness will happen in 8 to 11 repetitions.

Continue for 2 minutes. To end, inhale, exhale and relax.

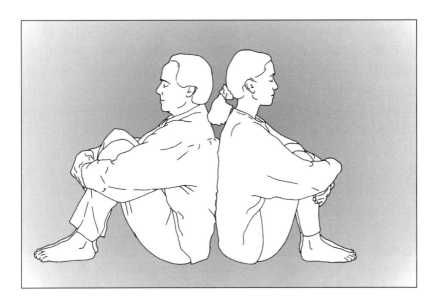

TO GET RID OF GRUDGES

Sit back to back with your partner, knees up, arms around your knees. Meditate on your heart. Hear it. Meditate on the sun. Bring it into your heart. Burn out all the bitterness you've felt through the years.

Continue for 3 minutes. To end, inhale, exhale and relax.

MEDITATION FOR TOTAL DIVINE HORNINESS – To Do
Before Sex

This meditation will free up your creativity and is in four parts.

For the first part sit in Easy Pose. The eyes are closed, focused at the third eye point. Mentally create the intention of realizing your true value. Imagine that you are the creation and the creator and meditate on your creative principle. Feel love for your physical body and mentally caress and kiss every part. Feel you are in union and a beautiful link with the cosmos. Your soul is in intercourse with the universal soul. Continue this for 15 minutes.

Feel total Divine Horniness. Then stretch every part of your body for 3 minutes.

The second part is Brahm mudra: Sit in easy pose, palms on the chest. The nipples are exactly in the center of the palms. Only the middle fingers are touching (Fig. 1). With every breath, and as the chest expands under the palms, feel the gift of life within you. Play and talk with the breath. Be grateful for it. Continue 3-11 minutes.

Fig. 1

For the third part place hands in Gyan mudra at the chest, thumb and forefinger forming an "O" in front of the nipples. The remaining fingers are together, extended straight out in Vishnu mudra (Fig. 2). Breathe long and deep for 3 minutes. When completed, stretch for 3 minutes.

Fig. 2

For the final part, the man and woman are sitting facing one another. The woman begins by chanting **EK ONG KAAR SAAT NAAM SIREE**. The man responds with **WHAA HE GURU G.O.D**. This continues with no pauses between partners for 3 minutes.

(Note: **EK** in this chant rhymes with "neck." The "O" in **ONG** rhymes with "go," and the "ng" is nasalized by blocking the back of the throat with the tongue touching the back part of the roof of the mouth. If chanted correctly, the vibration will tickle the back of your throat, and you will feel a humming at the third eye. **G.O.D** is pronounced like the English letters of the alphabet.)

The Art of Making Sex Sacred

THE SACRED ART OF MAKING LOVE

If love is the key to happiness, then lovemaking is truly the most spiritual activity, allowing access to the secret recesses of the heart. Of course, lovemaking is not strictly limited to the act of sexual intercourse. Since making love involves all the senses, it makes sense to use all our faculties to enhance the ultimate experience of physical union. In the yogic tradition, the act of sex doesn't start in the bedroom. Intercourse is the final act in the drama which starts in the impulse of the spirit the "urge to merge" according to Yogi Bhajan. The stimulus for lovemaking must take place at least 72 hours before the actual consummation. A woman is multi-dimensional, complex and subtle. The core of her essence is spirit. Therefore, lovemaking must begin when two people consciously set aside the time to create a nurturing, uplifting and safe environment in which to explore the mysteries of their hearts, minds, bodies, and souls.

"Nobody can afford to be lustful. But everybody must love. Without love you can never find your life, and with lust you can never enjoy life."–Yogi Bhajan

Making Love a Meditation

In our stress-filled, busy lives it is often difficult to come together with our partner in a relaxed, calm way. If sex is to be experienced as "sacred," couples must consciously prepare ahead of time. The following yogic techniques offer a framework for setting a peaceful, loving vibration, thus opening a conscious pathway for the sacred journey of sex to take place. Most important, though, the techniques are secondary to the loving intent and the conscious caring.

Make sure the bedroom is clean, with perhaps some incense and candles. Choose some appropriate music. A cozy, secure environment is especially important to the woman. Only light meals should be eaten that day. Yogurt drinks are perfect. Special drinks for after intercourse can be prepared ahead of time. (See Appendix A: Sexy Foods).

Kundalini Yoga kriyas or individual exercises can be practiced beforehand to open the energy centers, followed by a Venus Kriya to harmonize your vibrations and see the soul in each other. Sit across from each other and meditate on the soul of your partner. Take time to drop the facade of the personality and allow your soul mate to see beyond the day-to-day reality into the essence of your Divine Being. Share your dreams, memories and fantasies with each other. Then, take time (ideally 2-3 hours) to explore, play, and harmonize your auras, through all the senses. Remember, we can touch each other by stimulating the skin, but we also "touch" with smell, sound, sight and taste. Go on a sensual picnic in order to fully arouse the sixth sense which allows the merging of the beings.

Getting to Know Each Other

One effective technique for couples who are building a trusting and comfortable relationship with one another is "stroking." This light touching technique can begin with clothes on or off. The couple simply lies together and lightly strokes each other, avoiding the most erogenous areas, like the breasts and genitals. The evening can end there, with a hug and a kiss. No intercourse need take place. It is a relaxed time with no expectations of performance. This stage can continue as long as the couple desires. It is a good time to use visualization and fantasy techniques.

As you stroke your partner, you can imagine that you are playing a harp or dancing over the body. Visualize harmony and joy between you and your partner. As you are being stroked, feel as though ocean waves are rippling over your body, soothing and healing you. Trust will develop between the couple, which is a prerequisite for a deeper and more satisfying sexual relationship.

Stroking can also be effectively used by a couple that has been together for a long time, but who need to reestablish their trust, or who wish to rejuvenate a stale relationship. Visualization and fantasy can be effective tools to bring new excitement into such a relationship.

In the next stage, stroking is continued in the nude, but this time as you stroke your partner's shoulder, feel it in your shoulder. As you stroke his buttocks, feel it in yours as well. The genitals can be approached but retreated from after brief encounters. Repeat this technique for as many encounters as desired, with each one lasting as long as time permits. There is still no intercourse. This technique builds control, especially if navel and rectal pumping or locks are applied to push the energy up into the higher centers.

Finally, when the couple is ready, stroking arouses the entire body, including the genitals, approaching and retreating, back and forth. The previous techniques can be applied here to raise the energy up to the higher centers. Lovemaking can be prolonged indefinitely using these methods. Use fantasy and imagery to enhance the experience. Avoid fantasies that take you away from the present moment, such as imagining that your partner is a past lover or a favorite movie star. Incorporate fantasies that bring you closer to your partner and enrich your experience of intimacy.

When intercourse does occur, let yourself lie still with your partner, feeling the merging of the energies. At this point of intercourse, there is an ecstatic feeling or "floating," which is like a blissful meditation. During this time you can ask questions of your Higher Self. Perhaps there is a challenge in your life which needs a solution. Put out the challenge and then allow the solution to come to you. When one is so powerfully charged with this atomic sexual energy, and the heart is open, then the conscious mind is temporarily on hold, while the unconscious is alive and sensitive. In such a state, a person can be totally open to the lessons of one's Higher Self.

Massage as Foreplay

If a woman's aura is increased to seven feet it will energize the man, instead of depleting him after sexual intercourse. By massaging and relaxing the woman, she will experience her expansive self, allowing a greater receptivity to her Higher Self.

There are nine areas in a woman and seven in a man, that can be massaged and stimulated before intercourse. These areas are in a particular order, but should be returned to and stimulated gently over time. Experiment with different types of touch. Sometimes a slow, light touch is more arousing than a "passionate" once-over. A woman's sensitivity in these areas also changes every 2 1/2 days. One night, her breasts may be the most sensual, another time her lips or the ears. Discovering which areas are the most sensitive at a particular time can be an adventure.

Massage for a Woman

1. Massage and caress the **breasts**, going from the outside inwards. A woman's breasts have to be lavishly prepared and aroused before the nipples themselves welcome touch.

2. Massage, caress, and kiss the **neck**. Moving upwards will excite her sexual energy.

3. The **lips** are very important. They possess an abundance of nerve endings and they are the key to the heart. You can spend a lot of time kissing the lips and using the lips to tantalize other areas of the body.

4. Using the lips, the tongue, or the hand, gently caress the **cheeks**.

5. The **ears** are very sensitive and possess numerous meridian points. The fingers, lips and tongue can play with the ears to awaken their sensuality.

6. Amply supplied with nerve endings, the **spine** is also extremely sensitive to sensual arousal. In my experience and that of workshop participants, it is also pleasurable if the man uses his hands, lips, tongue or

penis, beginning at the lower spine, moving the energy up to the neck.

7. The woman's **inner thighs** are very sensitive to touch, and they are the outer gates to one of her most erogenous areas, her clitoris. Preparing the woman by caressing and kissing the inner thighs can be an extremely pleasurable experience.

8. We don't normally think of the **calves** as an erogenous area. Actually, the whole area from the heels and up the calves possesses meridians points which are very important for the woman's whole reproductive system. It is essential for her reproductive health to have this area massaged and stimulated on a regular basis.

9. A woman will be much more willing to open the doors of her **clitoris** and **vagina** if she has been fully stimulated in the other areas first. Because the nerve endings at this area are the most concentrated, touch here can be the most ecstatic. Nevertheless, if she is not sufficiently aroused, touch here can actually be irritating.

A woman's entire body should be stimulated and aroused. Erogenous areas of the body include much more than the breasts and clitoris. Take the time to joyously discover these areas together.

Massage for a Man

There are seven areas to stimulate in a man. These areas will first relax him and then slowly arouse him. A man's fire is ignited quickly; a woman's waters boil slowly. Therefore, a man needs to be stimulated carefully, in order to avoid over-arousing him.

1. Massage and stimulate his **head** and **hair**. This is very relaxing.

2. Spend much time at the **lips**, combined with the other areas.

3. Begin massaging and stroking at the top of the **neck**. Then go down the **spine**. Roll the skin with the fingers as you go down. Whereas the woman's spine is massaged up to arouse her, the man's spine is massaged down to help calm his energy.

4. The **buttocks** region is very important. Men store a lot of tension in this area. Massage this area firmly, especially in the groove along the outside of the buttocks.

5. Inside the **thighs** and the **testicles**. Watch that the touch is not too arousing. Light touch will help him keep control.

6. The **penis**. Again, be careful not to over stimulate him.

7. The **navel** and **chest** area, including the **nipples**, is very sensitive and arousing in a man.

As with women, these areas can be aroused repeatedly, going back and forth from the more sensitive ones to those less erotic. The tongue, lips, breasts, and hands can be used to excite and caress various areas. There are no rules in sex, as long as both partners agree and no one gets hurt.

Breath Harmony

Male and female should harmonize the breath before engaging in sexual intercourse. The breath is very important. The man should be breathing predominantly through his right nostril and the woman through her left nostril. To change nostril breathing, put pressure in the armpit of the opposite side you want to be breathing. For example, if you are breathing predominantly through the right nostril, but you want to breathe through the left, put pressure in the right armpit with your left hand. The breath should change within 3 minutes and remain steady for 2-1/2 hours. The breath should also be long, deep, and slow. Slowing the breath down as much as possible will also help to prevent premature ejaculation. It helps bring more control during intercourse. Long deep breathing with Circular Visualization is also excellent.

Intercourse

Only after all her areas have been stimulated should the woman be entered. Her spine should be cool, his will be sweating. There are different positions of the clitoris and vagina, which will affect the position of entry.

Lower: 60% of women have lower entry, which means the clitoris is distant from the vagina opening. In order to enter her with the man on top position, her buttocks will have to be raised 6-12 inches. The man can also enter from the back or she can be on top. Intercourse may be painful for her if the man is on top, and the buttocks are not raised.

Upper: 30% of women have an upper entry, (the clitoris is close to the vagina opening). She reaches orgasm easily, and lubricates in large quantities. Man on top is the best position.

Middle: 10% of women have middle entry, and intercourse is the easiest for both involved. Any position is good.

A woman should only be entered when her breasts are tense and the nipples erect. The man should enter slowly, hold her at the lower spine and rotate. This rotation causes all the nerves to be stimulated. There will be a suction sound and a pulling. This rotary movement defies age, because the muscles of the vagina mouth are kept tight. In this rotary motion, the woman also benefits, because there is less change of pressure on the hip bones. As her hips are capable of opening for childbirth, during sexual intercourse (where her muscular system relaxes) improper movement could place physical pressure on her hips, which can cause hip, back, and circulation problems.

It can also be very pleasurable, with prolonged ejaculation, if the man does not move. He holds the woman at the lower spine, while she contracts and relaxes her vaginal muscles. Both can pull the rectum muscles, sending the energy up, while focusing at the third eye. The man can also retreat for a time, allowing his energy to subside. This would be a good time for Circular Breathing.

Mind is the Biggest Sex Organ

Think of all the occasions you have fantasized an entire scenario around sex. You may have been visualizing a fictitious or an actual partner. You may have created a place, a time, how he or she looked, felt and responded to you. Using your visualization only, you probably became aroused, maybe even reached orgasm. We can use these tools of self-suggestion to create real situations. Instead of just dreaming, why not use the power of the mind to improve your sexual enjoyment in real life? Imagine you are on a secluded beach and are touching each other for the first time. Be creative and have fun with it.

If the couple is working with trust issues, positive affirmations and visualizations can be effective as well. Imagine what it would look like and feel like if there was trust. Ask your Higher Powers to help you.

Two Techniques to Help Him Keep Control

The squeeze method. The woman or the man can hold the penis firmly at the base and squeeze. When the overwhelming urge to ejaculate subsides, then release the hold.

When the man feels he is losing control, either partner can press on the bulge between the scrotum and the rectum until he regains control. The finger pressure has to be quite firm.

These techniques should not be done when ejaculation is imminent.

Raising the Energy Up to the Higher Centers

During the arousal stage of love-making, both the woman and the man can pull Mul Bandh or pump the rectum, breathing in short sniffs and focusing the eyes at the third eye point (similar to the 4/4 breath technique in Chapter 5). When perfected, focusing the energy upwards can produce wonderfully blissful results.

The above technique has four advantages. First, it prolongs orgasm and ejaculation, so that a couple can extend the lovemaking encounter. Second, this technique enhances erotic feelings. Third, it creates a spiritual union at the higher centers. Fourth, when the orgasm comes, if the couple decides to let the energy go down and out, it is much more intense and pleasurable.

The G-Spot

In the Taoist tradition, there is acknowledgment of the sensitive G-spot. Surrounding the urethra is a plexus of blood vessels, which engorge and bulge during sexual excitement. This bulge is the G-spot. It can be reached by feeling around the front and upper part of the inside of the vagina, one-half inch deeper than a woman's middle finger. It is difficult for a woman's G-spot to be stimulated with the man on top. A rear entry or the woman on top are the easiest positions to reach her G-spot.

The Sitting Position

This position is described in all the yogic and Taoist books as being effective in raising the energy. The rectum and navel can be pulled in, focusing at the third eye. Let the energy float up and enjoy the ecstasy.

Taoist Locking Method

This method is an ancient Taoist teaching used by a man to control his ejaculation and to preserve his semen.

When the man is having intercourse, he can make three shallow thrusts and one deep thrust with his penis to maintain control. As he builds up control, over time, he can work up to nine shallow thrusts and one deep thrust. The breath should be long and deep through the nose so that he will not start panting. This breath will help him keep control.

If he feels that he may soon lose control, the man can lift his waist slightly and remove his penis from the vagina one inch or more, staying still. The breath should be deep and from the diaphragm. At the same time, he should contract his lower abdomen. Upon regaining his control, he can resume thrusting.

It is very important that the man retreats when he first becomes excited. It is better to retreat too early than too late. By practicing this method, a man can easily control his ejaculation as long as he wants. He can decide to ejaculate or not. A man should never try to prevent an ejaculation when it is "beyond-the-beyond" point, as this can lead to kidney or prostrate problems. Caution and consciousness must be followed when practicing these methods. It is not a yogic practice to prevent ejaculation altogether.

Using the Sexual Energy to Heal the Body

Anyone who has had experience with energy flow during meditation, acupuncture, massage, polarity therapy, Jin Shin Do or other body work is familiar with its healing potential. Sexual energy is the most powerful energy of all and can be used for healing. During intercourse, after the energy is easily flowing up and down and both partners have good control, is a good time to practice this form of healing. Each person can put their hands on the area of their partner in need of healing, focusing the healing energy to flow through their hands. The hands may tingle and the body feel warm and soothed. You can also practice Circular Breathing at this time.

Another method of healing during sex would be to mentally send healing energy to the other person and to one's self during intercourse and immediately after the climax.

After the Climax

"Any time you (woman) have sexual intercourse, you have to stretch yourself to bring yourself into balance. If you refuse to do it you may be off balance for one week." – Yogi Bhajan

It is very important to follow certain practices following intercourse, to reset the electromagnetic field, and continue the lovemaking experience. It is important that the auras of the two intermix during this time. Both should keep their spine and organs warm. Usually the woman has more energy, so she can massage, embrace, and kiss her partner. Keep the physical entanglement going on until somebody falls asleep. Engage in pillow talk about dreams and memories, not information or discussion at this time.

Before falling asleep, the man should urinate and wash his sex organ in warm water. Then he should enjoy the special sesame-ginger drink (Appendix A: Sexy Foods). If this is taken within 45 minutes after ejaculation, it replenishes his sperm and energy.

After climax, the woman needs to take care of herself to bring equilibrium to her aura. During intercourse, if a woman has climaxed before the man, she will sweat as he keeps pumping. Afterwards, if she rubs this sweat into her skin it will be reabsorbed by the body, which is very healthy. In addition, there are nine things she should do to re-set her aura after sex.

Go to the bathroom and urinate. This changes the nostril breathing, which neutralizes the energy.

Wash the face with cold water.

Wash the armpits with a wet towel to balance the parasympathetic nervous system.

Wash the inner thighs.

Wash behind the ears.

Wash the feet with a wet towel.

Brush the teeth.

Stretching exercises. Bundle roll is a must for bringing the balance. Lie down with legs together and arms next to your sides and roll over and over, keeping the body straight. Without doing this, the energy will be off for one week.

Lastly, meditate. This will keep the energy high, eliminating any negative or strange vibrations from penetrating her aura and getting lodged there.

At this point it is nice to return to bed to resume cuddling. Some women are so energized from lovemaking that they cannot sleep. But if a woman is tired, she can drift into sleep. It is best if the woman can take 11-30 minutes to do the techniques above before she falls asleep. If she does fall asleep, she can do them when she awakens.

The Altar of Loving

By consciously preparing for the act of sacred sex, and through loving, conscious practice, all couples can elevate their relationship through the gift of making sacred love. One way to return that energy to the Universe, so that the gift can continue to be received, is to place a gift on the Altar of Loving. This can be a physical altar, which you can create in a cozy corner of your home and decorate with flowers, crystals, pictures and candles. Or, it can be a place in your heart where you place loving thoughts. The act of taking the very real feelings and experiences of ecstatic sexual union and relating them to a Higher Power creates a loving union that blissfully binds you to a greater purpose and relationship with Creation. Even if things get rocky in your earthly relationship, your Soul is always relating to its marriage with the Infinite.

With your partner, you can create a ritual of renewal and gratitude. You may simply want to ask the Universe to bless your union. You may want to perform an act of selfless service or giving to someone else as an act of gratitude. The ceremony of making love a sacred experience has a final act, after the physical climax, of returning the blessing to the Mother Earth and Sky Father. Just as a man and woman come together to create new life, so your act of loving can be consecrated to rebirth, healing and bringing peace to the earth. Take a few moments to return the blessing of Light, so that all the creatures of the earth and heavens will be blessed through your sacred act of loving.

Appendix A:
Sexy Foods

Diet greatly relates to our sexual energy. Food is supposed to supply the body with the nourishment it needs; not rob it of its vitality and vigor. If the body is heavy, clogged, sluggish and struggling, sex will be less creative, blissful, healing and fun. Normally it takes about one-third of the body's energy to digest food. Therefore, before sexual intercourse, it is best if the diet is light, nutritious and easy to digest. You can include plenty of fresh fruits and vegetables, whole grains, nuts and seeds, beans, and milk products or milk substitutes. In addition, certain foods have been effectively used to promote sexual health throughout the ages.

In this section there are foods that are good for male potency and sexual health, but can be enjoyed by women also, as well as foods for female radiance and vitality. Many of the foods or ingredients can usually be purchased at health food stores, East Indian food shops, or through specialty food catalogs. (See Resource section on page 119.)

SEXY FOODS FOR MEN

One of the worst things a man can do for his sexual potency is to overeat. A man should never fill his stomach more than three-quarters full. As a general guideline, a man should not have sex immediately following a heavy meal. For optimal sexual function, a liquid diet during the day is best prior to sexual intercourse. If this is not possible, wait four hours after eating before having sex.

The following foods are especially effective for men in increasing their potency, correcting sexual dysfunction, and maintaining sexual vitality.

Almonds

Almonds help to maintain a man's potency. Here is a delicious breakfast drink to enjoy.

1 cup milk
6 peeled almonds (soak overnight, then blanch before peeling)
Seeds from 3 cardamom pods, crushed
1/2 tsp. honey
"Kisses are like almonds." – Maltese proverb

Banyan Tree Milk

The sap from the banyan tree is excellent for semen production, is recommended for semen leakage in the urine, and is helpful in correcting premature ejaculation. Take six drops with a teaspoon of honey in yogurt for six days. For best results, abstain from sex for six to eight days before the treatment and eight to ten days afterwards. The best time of year to practice this treatment is in the early spring or fall. In America, banyan tree milk is available in health food stores in Florida and Hawaii, in East Indian food shops, or by mail order (see Resources on page 119).

Date Milk

This wonderful drink helps restore general health, vigor and rejuvenation and is recommended for men to drink following sex.

8 oz. milk (or non-dairy milk substitute)
6 dates

Slice dates in half. Simmer in milk on a very low heat for 20 minutes, stirring occasionally. Strain and serve. Serves 1. Prepare this drink ahead of time and keep warm in a thermos or on a hot plate next to the bed.

Appendix A: Sexy Foods

Fresh Figs

Good for sexual or nervous disorders, eat 10–15 figs with yogurt.

Golden Figs

For men, this is a good potency recipe. Women can enjoy them as well. Do not eat more than three per day, morning, afternoon and evening.

10–15 fresh figs

1/2 cup milk

1 Tbsp. saffron

1 clean syringe (available at the pharmacy without the needle)

Soak saffron overnight in the milk. In the morning, blend the milk and the saffron until smooth. Carefully wash the figs. Draw the milk and saffron into the syringe and inject the "nectar" into the figs. These can be stored in the freezer.

"Figs can make you a sexual pig." – Yogi Bhajan

Garlic

Stimulates the production of semen. Best taken raw, but is also effective if slightly cooked. Garlic capsules are also available.

Garlic Toast

Here's a tasty way to enjoy garlic. It makes a good breakfast food.

2 slices whole grain bread

2–4 medium cloves garlic (more can be used)

Peel and thinly slice garlic. Lightly toast bread in toaster. Spread liberally with ghee. Top with garlic slices. Place in broiler or toaster oven for no more than 5 minutes. For variety, top with a thin slice of cheese before broiling.

Ghee

This is the oil of choice for a man. Ghee (clarified butter) aids semen production and can be used like any cooking oil or butter without contributing to weight problems.

How to Make Ghee. On the stovetop, simmer butter in a pot for about 10–20 minutes. Use at least two pounds of butter, to avoid burning. While cooking, skim off the white foam from the top, leaving a clear yellow liquid. Pour only the clear ghee into a container without letting any of the white sediment at the bottom of the pan slide in. Store at room temperature and use as you would butter or cooking oil. Ghee may also be prepared in a crock pot on a low temperature.

Ginger

Good for general sexual strength, ginger root taken as juice, raw, or cooked in food or raw builds a strong nervous system. Ginger sauteed in ghee on yams is fantastic. Many yogic and oriental dishes are prepared with ginger.

Sesame–Ginger Milk

This creamy and stimulating drink is nourishing to the nervous system and to the male sex organs. It is best taken within 45 minutes after sexual activity to replenish male energy and seminal fluids.

¼ cup raw sesame seeds

2 tbsp. fresh ginger root (peeled and coarsely chopped or juiced)

12 oz. milk, warmed

2 tsp. honey or maple syrup

To prevent the ginger from splitting the milk, warm the milk first, then blend ginger in the milk (do not boil ginger in the milk). Blend ingredients at high speed until smooth and frothy. Makes about 2 cups.

Lecithin

Two to three tablespoons of lecithin a day, taken on cereal, vegetables, grains or blended in a protein drink, increases semen production.

Mangoes

This tasty tropical fruit, very popular in India, is used for impotence and sexual weakness. They should be eaten with milk or yogurt.

Appendix A: Sexy Foods

Mango Lassi
This is a delicious and refreshing drink for both women and men.

2 cups homemade yogurt

2 medium mangoes (very ripe)

3 Tbsp. maple syrup or honey

6 ice cubes

Peel and slice mangoes. Put all ingredients in a blender and blend at high speed. If fresh mangoes aren't available, use frozen mango chunks. Serves 4–6.

Nutmeg
This spice is used for premature ejaculation. The whole nutmeg (not powdered) must be used, grated and put in a drink or yogurt. One to two teaspoons of freshly grated nutmeg can be put in a few ounces of yogurt and taken 4 hours before intercourse. Do not take nutmeg if you have or suspect you have low blood pressure. Under no circumstances should one take more than one nut unless it is done under the direction and care of a health professional. It is best to only take nutmeg when one has time to relax. Driving is not advisable. Nutmeg grated and blended in a milk shake with banana is delicious.

Banana–Nutmeg Drink or Ice Cream
1 cup milk

3 medium-size ripe bananas

1 whole nutmeg, ground

1 fresh apple, cored and peeled

¼–½ cup honey (optional)

Grind nutmeg with a mortar and pestle, a grinder, or grater. Blend ingredients until smooth. Serve hot or cold as a drink or pour into an ice cream maker and churn until ready. Makes 1 quart.

Onions
Part of the "trinity root" of onions, garlic, and ginger recommended for health and vitality, onions also increase semen production and

sexual energy. Raw onion juice is best, but it is also good in food. (See *Potent Potatoes* recipe for preparation of trinity root masala, sauteed in ghee, which can be used as a seasoning for vegetables and other yogic dishes with vegetables and legumes.)

Potent Potatoes

This recipe is made with a masala (mixture) of "trinity" roots – onions, ginger and garlic – which work together to purify the blood, strengthen the nervous and immune systems, promote elimination and give energy.

4 russet baking potatoes
½ cup ghee
3 onions, chopped
¼ cup ginger, minced
1 bulb garlic, minced
1 tsp. black pepper
1 ½ tsp. turmeric
1 tsp. crushed red chilies or cayenne
8 whole cloves
Seeds of 3 cardamon pods
½ tsp. ground cinnamon
⅓ cup tamari soy sauce or Bragg Liquid Aminos
½ pint cottage cheese
4 slices cheese, cut in half
1 bell pepper, finely diced
½ cup pineapple, chopped and drained

Bake potatoes for about 1 hour, until soft on the inside and crispy on the outside. Meanwhile, heat ghee in skillet. Add onions and ginger. Saute until onions are well done, then add garlic and spices. If spices are sticking to the pan, add more oil or water. Cook until browned. Add soy sauce. Cut baked potatoes in half lengthwise. Scoop out the insides and combine with the masala. Add cottage cheese to this mixture. Refill potato shells forming mounds on top. Cover with slices of cheese and broil until melted and golden. Garnish with bell peppers and pineapple. Serves 4–8.

"P" Fruits

"P" fruits are good for a man's creativity, including peaches, plums, pineapples, pears, persimmons and papayas blended thoroughly with yogurt. Bananas can also be included.

Pistachios

These tasty nuts should be in every man's diet. Eat one handful a day, raw, unsalted and unskinned.

Saffron

This exotic spice gives a man vitality. It can be used for skin and hair problems, old age, senility and general vigor.

Saffron–Almond Rice

1 cup milk

½ tsp. cinnamon

1 tsp. saffron

1 tsp. salt

1 ½ cups Basmati rice

½ cup almonds

6 cloves garlic

1 tbsp. ghee

2 cups homemade yogurt

To guard against viral infections, add the following seeds

1/6 cup watermelon seeds

1/6 cup zucchini seeds

1/6 cup pumpkin seeds

Soak saffron in milk overnight. In the morning, blend until smooth. Soak almonds overnight or in boiling water to remove the skins. Then slice almonds. Peel and slice garlic cloves in quarters. Saute garlic and almonds in ghee. Rinse rice thoroughly. Boil rice in saffron milk and 2 cups water. Add the saffron milk when the rice is half-cooked. Add garlic and almonds. Simmer for 20 minutes. Serve with yogurt.

Sarsaparilla

This herb enhances sexual potency and is a natural source of male and female sex hormones. As a liquid extract, sarsaparilla can be used to make traditional root beer blended with honey and carbonated mineral water.

Sunflower Seeds

Eaten raw, on salads or sprouted, these seeds are an excellent natural source of Vitamin E and Zinc, which play an important role in the growth and maturity of male sex glands and the prostate gland.

Yogi Tea

This healthful blend of spices is a delicious and healthful way of restoring the nervous system, purifying the blood, increasing potency and is a digestive aid. It is a great coffee substitute. Make a big potful and store it in the refrigerator.

2 quarts water

15 whole cloves

20 green cardamom pods (slightly crushed)

20 black peppercorns

3 sticks cinnamon

8 slices ginger root

½ tsp. black tea (optional)

3 cups milk

Bring water to a boil in a 3–4 quart pot. Add spices, cover and boil gently for 20–30 minutes until a deep reddish brown. Add black tea. Cool and strain tea. To drink, add milk or soy milk, return to a boil and immediately remove from heat. Add sweetener to taste. Or store without milk in the refrigerator. Then just add the milk a cup at a time. Yogi Tea can also be purchased loose or in tea bags at health food stores.

Rejuvenating Foods After Sex

Following sexual intercourse, it is important for a man to eat special foods to replenish his sexual fluids and to strengthen his nervous system. Yogi Tea, Sesame–Ginger Milk and Date Milk are excellent.

SEXY FOODS FOR WOMEN

Men and women are different in many ways. Diet is no exception. Men and women require different foods and eating habits. The most important thing women have to consider is elimination. Whatever a woman eats should be eliminated within eighteen hours. Foods that are especially dangerous to a woman's health and radiance are meat, alcohol, caffeine, sugar, salt, eggs, saturated fats, and heavy cheeses.

In general, the ideal eating pattern for a woman is to eat two solid meals and two liquid meals a day. Breakfast can be a light, thick drink made of milk or juice. Lunch can be anything she can digest easily. A second thick drink can be taken in the afternoon. Dinner should be light, such as steamed vegetables, salad, and soups.

Almonds

Eaten soaked and peeled, almonds are an excellent source of protein and B vitamins. Women should eat a handful daily with raisins (a good source of natural iron) as a tasty "stress-buster" snack.

Sauteed Almonds

This tasty treat can be prepared on the days a woman is menstruating. The tannic acid in the skins of the almonds help the shedding of the uterine lining during her period. Saute a handful of unpeeled raw almonds in ghee. When lightly toasted, add a teaspoon of honey until caramelized.

Eggplant

This is a woman's food. It can be eaten one week before the onset of her period to help regulate menstrual flow. It also energizes her whole system.

Eggplant Pakoras

Eggplant is the "sexiest" food for women. This delicious Indian batter-fried eggplant dish helps regulate a woman's menstrual flow.

1 eggplant (peeled)

2 tsp. tamari

2 cups garbanzo flour

1 tsp. black pepper

1 tbsp. caraway seeds

¼ tsp. ground cloves

1 tsp. oregano seeds (ajwain)

½ cup milk

1 tsp. cardamon seeds

¾ cup onion, juiced or pureed

½ tsp. cinnamon

⅓ cup water

2 tsp. turmeric

¼ cup honey

Cut peeled eggplant in ⅜ inch slices and soak for 15–20 minutes in a bowl of salt water to remove bitterness. Mix all spices with the garbanzo flour. Add onion and milk to the flour mixture and blend with a fork into a smooth, thick batter, removing all lumps. Dip the eggplant slices in the batter and fry in vegetable oil or ghee until they are golden brown. Set on a paper towel to drain and then serve with tomato catsup or chutney. Serves 4–6.

Fruit

Fruits of all kinds are excellent for women. Especially good are apricots, peaches, plums, persimmons, papayas, figs, pears, bananas, pomegranates, and oranges. Persimmons enhance a woman's sexual energy. Mangos are good for menstrual disorders . Fruit is healing for the entire female sexual system. Pickled mango is one of the most powerful sexual foods for a woman. Mangos are a very acidic food, so it is best to eat them with milk or yogurt (see *Mango Lassi*).

Appendix A: Sexy Foods

Ginger

Fresh ginger root is a woman's best friend. Ginger tea can be taken to relieve menstrual cramps and strengthen the nervous system. Grate or thinly slice about 2 inches of fresh ginger root (peeled or unpeeled) into one quart of water. Simmer for 10 minutes. Drink with a little milk and honey. Yogi Tea, made with extra ginger is also excellent. Ginger, prepared as a masala with onions and garlic is also good for overall nerve strength (see *Potent Potatoes*).

Green Chile

High in Vitamin C and chlorophyll, green chile prevents mouth odor during menstruation, aids digestion, and does not allow waste pockets to develop in the intestinal tract.

Green Vegetables

Eaten in a simple mono-diet for a few days (no other foods eaten), all green vegetables can help correct an irregular menstrual cycle.

"Ms. Whiz"

Here's a perfect breakfast drink for women. The daily dose of sesame oil or almond oil can go in this drink. Rice bran syrup contains all the essential minerals. Women should take some every day, in water or blended in a breakfast drink. Sesame oil, which is high in calcium, should be taken daily as well. This drink can also be used as a weight-loss drink by adding 2 tablespoons protein powder instead of the cold-pressed oil and drinking four times per day instead of meals.

1 ripe banana
8 oz. orange juice
1 Tbsp. liquid chlorophyll
2 tsp. rice bran syrup
2 tsp. cold-pressed almond oil or sesame oil
Blend until smooth and frothy.

Turmeric

This healing root is excellent for a woman's internal organs. It can purify a woman's blood, tonify the joints, and maintain the mucous membranes, especially in the female sex organs. At least two tablespoons or more of turmeric, a week, should be included in her diet.

Golden Milk

This delicious hot drink is very good for the spine. It lubricates all the joints and helps to break up calcium deposits. It is an excellent way for men and women to take turmeric.

1/8 tsp. turmeric (up to 1 tsp. according to taste)

¼ cup water

8 oz. milk (or non-dairy milk substitute)

2 Tbsp. raw almond oil

Honey to taste

Boil turmeric in water for about 8 minutes until it forms a thick paste. If too much water boils away, add a little more water. In another saucepan, bring the milk to a boil with the almond oil. As soon as it boils, remove from the stove. Combine the two mixtures and add honey to taste. For an extra treat, blend golden milk until frothy and serve with a pinch of cinnamon.

A "reserve supply" of turmeric paste can be kept on hand. Boil a large quantity of turmeric and store in the refrigerator for up to 40 days.

Yogi Tea

This refreshing drink is an absolute must for women. It purifies the blood, strengthens the nervous system, and energizes the body (see page 98).

APPENDIX B:
MORE YOGIC TEACHINGS ON SEX
BY YOGI BHAJAN

PHYSICAL ASPECTS OF SEX

At what age is a man ready for sex?

A man should ideally let his sex organs become mature before he engages in sexual activity, because the basic semen, the oil in his machine, is thin and not totally matured until that time (usually around age 24). Also, as the quality of the bone marrow is not fully matured, the bone structure is not yet properly developed. There can be problems with the bones later in life, especially in women, because of a calcium/mineral imbalance. If the man engages in sexual activity before he is physically and emotionally ready for the woman, his chances for impotency are much greater. In the West, man is not taught to respect his "seed." He is eager and encouraged to prove his virility as young as possible. By mid-life or sooner, many men are "spent" and experience periodic or complete impotency.

At what age is a woman ready for sex?

A woman's sexual organs are not fully developed until she is 16-17 years old. Under no circumstances should sexual activity be introduced mentally or physically until after that age. If the couple is too young, there will not be a blending of the Yin and Yang energy, which puts a pressure on the nervous system, creating negativity, especially in the woman. She is taking the risk of nervous or temperamental problems. Nervous problems can be corrected with vitamins and exercise and yoga. Temperamental problems can only be corrected with meditation.

Is the glandular system stimulated during sex?

Yes, and for this reason, it is not healthy to have too much sex or too little sex. The purpose of sexual activity is to create the interlocked vibration between the male and female. The glandular activity must accelerate to the point that it comes to the full optimum point, and thereafter there is complete relaxation.

What about personal hygiene?

It is essential for the woman to take a bath before intercourse. If there is any kind of odor, she should take a douche with a little turmeric and yogurt. Let the yogurt sit out for a couple of days to develop more acidophilus. This combination will take care of any bacteria. Men should clean their sexual organ before intercourse.

Sometimes during intercourse I feel pressure in my intestines. What's happening?

During intercourse, the lower colon and rectum should be empty. Even after a bowel movement if the rectum is not clear, an enema should be taken. If the woman's bowel is not clear, there could be discomfort in the vagina, and through the movement of the male organ, the stool could backtrack and damage the iliocaecal valve.

I am going to have a baby. What about circumcision?

The "butter of life" is the secretion which comes out of two incision-like marks on the man's penis. If a man is circumcised, the secretion can still be produced, but it cannot be stored. This secretion is the food of the woman's vagina. When they have intercourse it is plucked out by the woman's membrane which gives strength to her pituitary and pineal glands. Sometimes, after intercourse, a woman becomes very depressed, when the male organ does not supply her that "butter of life."

Not circumcising can present a problem with relatives who embrace religions which profess circumcision. But research shows that circumcision has no physical benefit, and it creates an unnecessary trauma for the infant. Parents must meditate on what is best for their child and sometimes face the wrath and ignorance of others.

When a male child is around three or four years in age, he can be taught to push back the foreskin and clean the area of the secretion. It is a very natural thing, like cleaning the ears of wax. When the boy takes his bath, he can clean himself.

What can be done about wet dreams?

Wet dreams create an imbalance in the nervous system and weaken the body for 3-4 hours or longer. One wet dream is equal to about six physical intercourses. The pressure of a wet dream on the nervous system is like the whole roof fell on a person. Because the stimulation is through the nervous system and mind, the body pays heavily for it.

To rejuvenate the body following a wet dream one can take a drink of hot water, lemon or orange and honey. Practicing Maha Bandh can also be helpful in preventing wet dreams.

What importance does the nervous system have in sex?

Before intercourse, the three nervous systems, sympathetic, parasympathetic and central should be in balance. If the sympathetic nervous system is out of balance, the man may experience premature ejaculation. If the parasympathetic nervous system is not functioning properly the man may not be able to have an erection. And if the central nervous system is out of balance he may have difficulty ejaculating at all. (See Chapter 5 for yoga exercises to strengthen sexual nerves.)

Should a man try to preserve his semen?

"In sexual love we have lost integrity. When we feel we are hungry, we are supposed to eat; so when we feel passionate, we feel we are supposed to have sex. That's what sexual love has become today. Man loses the sense of value and self-respect. When you do not value the seed, what do you value? A farmer who does not care for the quality of his seed, nor for the quality of his land and does not care to preserve the seed, or sow it in a proper line; do

you call him a good farmer?" – Yogi Bhajan

In sex it takes 80 drops of blood to make 1 drop of semen. So, for example, 50 drops of semen is equal to 4,000 drops of blood. This represents a man's physical as well as mental and emotional potency. (For a man to remain potent, he should massage between his sex organ and the anus after urinating or while showering.) If woman is only flesh, man can lose energy. But, if woman has a strong aura, at least seven feet, man can receive energy. Woman must help him preserve his seed, not waste or abuse it. This means that it is important for the woman to care for herself physically, emotionally and spiritually. If she is eating a healthy, cleansing diet, doing yoga, exercising, and meditating, she is more likely to have a strong auric body. Man is most attracted to woman's spirit not her flesh. If her spirit is bright, the man feels uplifted and great.

What is the yogic philosophy about masturbation?

Masturbation in men creates a triple action on the pituitary gland, which takes away his power to concentrate. It is a waste of his precious seed and energy. Women do not experience the same ill-effects as men. For women, it is more a matter of deciding how she wants to use her creative energy and focus. It is better for her to do some exercises to re-direct the "itchy" energy. This is not a moral issue as it is in some religions. In yogic philosophy we are concerned with bringing harmony between heaven and earth. The issue here is one of consciousness and energy concentration. In which chakra do you want your energy and consciousness to reside?

Then what can be done about horniness?

To feel horny is not a sin or wrong, but if one knows how to invoke the meditative mind, which raises the energy up, he can become totally creative. Horniness on the physical plane is sexual intercourse; on a higher plane it is creativity. It is the same energy, just in different centers of the body and used differently.

Meditation for Women to Neutralize Unwanted Horniness ("Neutral Nostril Kriya")

Sit in Easy Pose and tilt back the head. Bring the arms out at a 60-degree angle. Open the nose and mouth wide, open the self to the universe, and make the sound "ahh" 3 or 4 times (or as needed). Then inhale, exhale and relax.

Meditation for Men to Transform Horniness

If you are horny and can invoke the meditative mind, you can become totally creative. Do Kirtan Kriya as follows.

Sit in Easy Pose with the hands in gyan mudra at the knees. Meditate at the third eye point. The mantra is **SAA TAA NAA MAA**. As you chant **SAA**, touch the forefinger to the thumb. On **TAA**, touch the middle finger to the thumb. On **NAA**, touch the ring finger to the thumb. On **MAA**, touch the little finger to the thumb. As you chant each syllable, visualize energy entering the top of the head in an "L" shaped course out through the third eye point, projecting out to Infinity. This energy flows along the energy path called the golden cord, connecting the pineal and the pituitary glands.

Begin chanting in a normal voice for 5 minutes. Then whisper for 5 minutes. Vibrate the mantra silently for 10 minutes. Once again whisper for 5 minutes. Then chant in a normal voice for 5 minutes. When completed, take a deep inhale and stretch the hands up as far as possible, spreading the fingers wide. Stretch the spine and take several deep breaths. Relax.

So women have "tidings," not climaxes?

Women are very superior in their sexual capacity. A man's energy builds to the point of an explosion, or climax. Usually he then has to relax and start over. His capacity is one, two or three climaxes at one time. Women's sexual energy is very different. Once her sexual energy reaches a certain point, she experiences "tidings," like waves, peaking and receding. She can go on like this, indefinitely, until she or her husband collapse from exhaustion.

THE SUBTLETIES OF SEX

Explain the blending of the auras?

When a man and woman have intercourse, their Yin and Yang energies merge and their auras blend; it is a purification. The two people become a different third person. Woman is especially sensitive to the blending of auras. If she blends her aura with one person here and another there, her aura scatters to the extent that her true identity is lost. Her energy is very sensitive and this merging of auras can have a very destructive effect on her. She cannot hold on to her identity and becomes emotionally weakened. This is very prevalent in our culture. For woman, sexual freedom should not mean sexual exploitation; it should mean sexual preservation, choice and reverence. On the other hand, if there is love, commitment and respect between the two people, intercourse can have a very positive effect on her. She will feel creative, expansive, vital and secure.

My husband seems satisfied with only physical satisfaction. I also need an emotional fulfillment. And this creates conflict between us...why?

For a woman, sex is much more than the physical act. It is also an emotional fulfillment. She has to feel secure, cozy, protected and cared for. It is her basic nature as a woman. It is important for a man to understand this basic difference between them. If he can allow emotional intimacy in and outside the bedroom, her personal fulfillment and projection back to him will expand beyond his wildest expectations.

What is the importance of a woman's dress?

When you look sexy you draw sex. When you look radiant, you draw God. There's a clear-cut distinction between Venus and penis. You dress up for Venus or you dress up for penis. Be honest. When you sit down in front of the mirror, ask yourself one thing - 'What am I dressing for?' If you are dressing for a penis, just understand that out of a whole man it is not more than twelve inches. A man may weight 250 pounds. Are you going to relate to a 250 pound man or one pound of his flesh which hangs between his two legs? What will be your security? Is that love? Your projection gives a message. How long do you want to be called a chick, a bitch, a nag or a fox? Decorate yourself with divinity. Dress yourself with integrity. Fix yourself with the reality of life. You'll be priceless, the most valuable and the most revered, respected human being.

Are my thoughts during sex important?

The attitude brought into the bedroom is one of unity: "I am for you, you are for me." It's a natural flow. Each partner must look to the other as being a god or goddess. Thoughts should be divine and graceful, they affect the psyche. The woman's thoughts affect the man even greater than his thoughts affect her. If she thinks of another man or thinks badly of him, the next morning he will feel horrible. On the other hand, if the woman thinks that this man is divine, he will feel great and radiant.

Is there a best time of day to have sex?

No, except avoid sex between 3 am and 6 am. Because of the position of the sun with the earth, it is a very sensitive time of day. Any other time is fine. Avoid sex within three hours after eating, after physical exercise, when the woman is deeply menstruating, when you are under stress and when you are not in a secure place. It should not be done in haste and worry. You must be brought to the point that you relax and thereafter sleep.

SEX AND CHILDREN

When should I teach my child about sex?

Boys and girls should be taught, in a scientific, neutral way, all the facts about sex. It should be a part of their knowledge in preparing for adulthood. The knowledge should be age appropriate and presented in a way the child can understand. Let their questions and curiosity guide the way. No age is too young to begin this education.

On the other hand, under no circumstances should sexual activity be introduced mentally or physically under the age of 16 or 17. The sex organs are not fully mature. It can be very damaging to a young girl or boy to be treated like sexual objects. Under no circumstances should a friend or relative touch a young girl or boy improperly or talk ungracefully to them. Young people need to have graceful behavior modeled for them. When fathers treat their daughters with total respect and grace, girls will know what is expected from all boys and men. In this way, graceful behavior becomes the expected norm.

Is it alright for a child to be sleeping in the same room when my husband and I are making love?

No! Make sure children are sleeping in a separate room when you are making love. The energy between a man and woman during sex is very powerful and atomic. This energy is too intense for a child's psyche, which is very pure and needs protection.

What about sex during pregnancy?

This is a controversial topic, and it coincides with what we just discussed. Just as sexual energy is too intense for the young child, it is even more intense for the unborn child. Once the pregnant mother is about four months into her pregnancy, intercourse should stop. Let her pray and be one with the growing child within her.

Does this mean that intimacy, affection and touching stops?

No, not at all. In fact, it is very important that mom and dad are very affectionate with one another. The parents' love is the most important thing a baby experiences in the womb. It can overcome the negative effects of many stresses and traumas.

What if dad is very "horny" and irritable?

He can do a lot of yoga or strenuous exercise. Cold showers are great for his general health and they can "cool" him down. It is also fine for mom to use other ways to occasionally satisfy him sexually other than with intercourse. During these times, she can keep her vibration very elevated and pure by mentally chanting and projecting from her higher chakras.

Author's note: No matter how happy dad is about his wife's pregnancy, no matter how mature he is, it is common for men to feel rejected and neglected during this time. She looks, acts and talks differently than before the pregnancy. Her energy is going inward, instead of outward. While he may have been the center of her attention before, now she's preoccupied with her pregnancy. Her lack of interest in sex may only compound his frustration. Even though he may try to understand what she's going through, he can't. Mom is so engrossed in her pregnancy, and is probably getting all of the attention, that she may not even notice her husband's feelings of abandonment and dethronement. As self-absorbed as she may be, it is still important that she makes him feel taken care of and appreciated. Giving each other foot massages can be a sweet way to share intimacy during this time. Just having her acknowledge his sexual challenge can help a lot. Humor is also a great way to release built-up sexual tension.

The Art of Making Sex Sacred

APPENDIX C:
"SHE SAYS, HE SAYS"
SEXUALITY WORKSHOP NOTES

Dr. Guru Terath Khalsa teaches workshops on Spirituality and Sexuality. These workshops include much of the information in this book. Workshop participants practice various techniques, such as Kundalini Yoga, Meditations and Venus Kriyas. They also learn about foods for sexual potency and discuss issues of intimacy.

Usually, at some point in the workshop, after a sense of trust has been established, the men and women break up into separate, smaller groups. This gives everyone a chance to talk more intimately about issues important to them. To facilitate the dialogue, they are given questions to answer, which are to be presented to the whole group. The questions actually serve as a springboard to deeper communication. The following is a sampling of typical questions asked of workshop participants and their answers.

How do you contact your sensuality? (Sensuality here is defined as feelings of sexuality, but does not necessarily lead to sex.)

"She Says" - Women say that they experience their sensuality in different ways. Some say their feelings of sensuality are triggered by experiences in nature, such as hiking or watching a sunset. Others say taking luxurious bubble baths does it. Many agree that eating well, exercising and feeling fit, in general, contributes to the free flow of sensual feelings. Some women mention movement during sports activities, yoga or dance. Music, painting and other artistic expressions are also mentioned. Many of the women who meditate say that meditation stimulates their sensual energies. Even though the sight or presence of a man does stimulate sexual feelings, there is a consensus that most of their sensual experiences are triggered from within.

The discussion usually leads to deeper feelings about the acceptability of sensual feelings and what to do with the energy. Many say yoga, sports, artistic expression, and meditation help them channel the energy into creative pursuits without suppressing it.

"He Says" - Men say that being physically fit definitely helps them experience their sensuality in a more satisfying and balanced way. While they do mention some of the same experiences as the women, overall, they seem to agree that most of their sensual stimulation occurs from external forces. For example, the sight of a beautiful woman, her smell, imagining himself with her, the sound of her voice, all seem to ignite their feelings of sensuality. In general, the men seem to have much less difficulty accepting their sensuality than the women do.

What is important to you during lovemaking? What is the best part?

"She Says" - Women say the environment is very important to them, i.e. music, cleanliness, the right temperature, etc. Having enough time is a big priority. They don't want to feel rushed or feel that they have to perform. The cozy feelings of being loved and cared for are more important than just the outcome (orgasm). Spending time together and experiencing being close is most important.

"He Says" - Men agree that spending time together is a priority. While they like a cozy environment, they are not as likely to prepare it themselves. Although they mention all the same needs as women (coziness, not feeling rushed), most of the men also say that the eventual outcome is also a major goal. Men who have a spiritual orientation seem less attached to ejaculating every time. They discuss raising their energy. Some have chosen not to ejaculate on some occasions. They enjoy the power and ecstasy of merging their polarities with their partner.

What do you dislike about sex?

"She Says" - Women agree that being treated like just a piece of flesh and feeling forced or obligated is the worst part about sex. Some feel like victims, powerless to say no and express their resentment and anger in this situation. This usually leads the group to discuss self-dignity, knowing yourself and personal empowerment.

They also discuss not having enough time. They want a cozy experience, but with children and busy schedules, it is at times hard to create. Mentioned last is the difficulty of communicating their likes and dislikes in sex to their partner.

"He Says" - Men say the worst part of sex is when they know that their partner really isn't into it. Some experience a "spent" or empty feeling if their partner isn't with them in spirit. Another bad experience for the men is feeling used or manipulated, when their partner seems to be trying to get something else from them. Some men are frustrated about feeling they have to be the perfect playboy lover, always knowing exactly how to satisfy their partner. They also feel inhibited and afraid to talk about sex.

What is the most exciting part of sex?

"She Says" - Women say being treated gently and respectfully was a real "turn on." Many women liked to be teased and courted ahead of time, when the men send out subtle sexual and caring vibrations. Most of the women agree that a "macho" style is much less effective most of the time. They say soft caresses are usually more sensual than a rough touch.

Many women say that pleasing their partner is exciting, especially when they can be in control of the play activities. A male's response to a woman's stimulation is especially exciting for many women.

"He Says" - Men express that the woman's responses in lovemaking create a very erotic experience for them. The way a woman moves and smells, her sighs and moans of ecstasy, as well as her facial expressions are very stimulating. Men enjoy a woman's caresses, of course, but many say her reaction to his touch is just as pleasurable for them. Unlike the typical stereotype, most men say that a soft touch is at least as stimulating for them, which usually allows them to prolong their orgasm.

Men feel especially sexy when their partner treats them as though they are the most wonderful man in the world.

What have you always wanted to tell your partner about sex, but have been afraid to say?

"She Says" - Women want men to be sensitive to them and to treat them gracefully. They want to be able to voice their preferences and to be heard. They need to feel special and cared for.

"He Says" - Men say they would like to go slower in sex, making it a more spiritual experience. But since it is difficult for them to do this on their own, they would like their partner to help. They also don't want to feel as if they have to be the perfect sex pro; rather, they would like feel accepted for being who they really are.

What do you fear the most about sex?

"She Says" - Women express fear that they will feel isolated and alone while making love. What creates this feeling of isolation and loneliness? Many ideas are voiced including a lack of communication and understanding on a deep level; not being appreciated for herself; her partner not really being present with her. Some women fear sex is just a performance not based on authentic emotions.

"He Says" - Men seem to have two main fears. The fear of impotence or performance failure is a big concern for the majority of men, even if they know it isn't important to their partner. Secondly is the fear of rejection for a man when he makes advances towards a woman for sex.

What builds trust and intimacy?

"She Says" - Women experience that communicating with their partners in deeper, truthful ways builds trust and intimacy. Some say writing their thoughts about their partners is helpful for them. Letters, notes, and poems are used as a catalyst for release, discussion and understanding.

Other women say that being touched, without the expectation of orgasm, can enhance trust. Sometimes true intimacy can be expressed if the expectation of sexual performance is eliminated.

"He Says" - Men say that trust is built when they feel a consistency from their partner—when she is consistently supporting him and believes in him. A man wants his partner to see the divine in him and his highest potential. He feels strength in knowing that she is in his life to uplift him, not to bring him down or make him feel inadequate.

Conclusion

After the groups meet separately, they join together as one large group to share their experiences. It is very helpful for the men and the women to hear themselves and each other talk about such intimate issues. The sharing reinforces for many participants the fact that it is alright, in fact natural, to feel sexy and spiritual at the same time. For many, it is the first time they have listened to the opposite sex talk so openly and honestly about sex.

Dr. Khalsa is available to lead workshops and for phone consultations. For more information please write to:

Guru Terath Kaur Khalsa, Ph.D.
P.O. Box 845
Santa Cruz, NM 87567
E-mail: gts@newmexico.com

RESOURCES

Books:

Yogi Ji Press
P.O. Box 970
Santa Cruz, NM 87567
Tel: (505) 753-5086
Fax: (505) 753-9249
E-mail: nam@newmexico.com

Books and products based on the teachings of Yogi Bhajan:

Ancient Healing Ways
P.O. Box 130
Espanola, NM 87532
Tel: (505) 747-2860 or 1-800-359-2940
Fax: (505) 747-2868

Tapes and videos of Yogi Bhajan:

Golden Temple Enterprises
Box 13 Shady Lane
Espanola, NM 87532
(800) 829-3970 or (505) 753-0563

Banyan Tree Sap (male potency food supplement):

Healer's Choice Herbs
28 Shady Lane
Espanola, NM 87532
Tel: (505) 747-6415
Fax: (505) 747-7166
Internet: http://www.herbangel.com

Illustrations of sexual positions East and West:

Sexual Secrets and other books by Destiny Press

Classes and counseling:

Guru Terath Kaur Khalsa, P.h.D., New Mexico licensed in Clinical and
Marriage and Family Counseling. Available for private counseling and
telephone consultations for individuals, couples, and families. Available
to do workshops in your area on Sacred Sexuality, Yoga and Meditation,
Communication, The Chakras, and other topics of Yogic Humanology.
The Ancient Sound of the Gong audio cassette tape (known for its powerful healing).

Guru Terath Kaur Khalsa, P.H.D.
P.O. Box 845
Santa Cruz, NM 87567
E-mail: gts@newmexico.com

Kundalini Yoga teachers:

International Kundalini Yoga Teachers Association (IKYTA)
Route 2, Box 4 Shady Lane
Espanola, NM 87532
(505) 753-0423
E-mail: ikyta@newmexico.com

3HO International summer events:

(505) 753-6341 or 1-888-346-2420
E-mail: yogainfo@roadrunner.com

Amrit Nivas:

A vacation and spiritual retreat next to the Kundalini Yoga and
Healing center. Write for brochure.
P.O. Box 970
Santa Cruz, NM 87567
(505) 753-5086
E-mail: nam@newmexico.com

Resources

Resources on the web:

Amrit Nivas:	www.cyberzones.com/amritnivas
Sikhnet:	www.sikhnet.com
Kundalini Yoga IKYTA:	www.kundalini.com
Yogi Bhajan:	www.yogibhajan.com
3HO:	www.3ho.org
The Yogi Tea Company	www.yogitea.com
Electronic Bookstores:	www.amazon.com
	www.barnesandnoble.com

The Art of Making Sex Sacred

GLOSSARY

Ajna – Sixth chakra, located at the "third eye," or the point midway between the eyebrows.

Anahata – Fourth chakra, located at the heart center (thymus gland) at the sternum area.

Apana – Eliminative force; outgoing cleansing breath.

Arcline – Energy center across the hairline (and at a woman's breasts); halo.

Aura – Electromagnetic field surrounding the body, sometimes referred to as the eighth chakra.

Baby Pose – Yoga posture, sitting on the heels bring forehead to the floor, arms behind, relaxed at side and palms up.

Bandh – Translates as "lock," pulling muscles of certain areas to draw up the energy in the body.

Bij mantra – "SAAT NAAM," meaning Truth is my Identity, used as a seed affirmation to replace old, negative thought patterns.

Breath of Fire – Yogic breath technique, long deep breathing done rapidly while pumping the navel point.

Chakras – Energy centers along the spine, often pictured as spinning wheels or opening lotus flowers, which correspond with states of spiritual awareness.

Corpse Pose – Yoga posture, laying flat on back in a relaxed position, for deep relaxation.

Crow Pose – Yoga posture, squat down keeping the feet flat on the floor and almost touching the buttocks to the floor. Good for digestion.

Easy Pose – Easy, cross-legged sitting position for practicing yoga and meditation.

Ether – One of the five tattwas or elements (including air, water, earth, and fire). Relates to the fifth chakra, the throat center, and the power of speech, projection and vibration of Truth.

Gurmukhi – A language based on the ancient yogic science of sound vibration, often used in Kundalini Yoga mantras.

Gyan Mudra – Hand position for divine knowledge; touching the tip of the index finger to the tip of the thumb.

Ida – One of two nerve channels which intertwine around the central spinal nerve. Ida conducts the feminine (lunar) energy of the body. See Pingala.

Jalandhara Bandh – Neck lock.

Kriya – A combination of yogic postures, hand positions, breath and mantra or a set of yoga exercises designed to create a specific result.

Kundal – "Coil of the hair of the beloved."

Kundalini Yoga – The science of awareness, working directly on your total energy, including your sexual energy.

Life Nerve –	Nerve which runs along the back of the leg from the buttocks to the heels; regulates emotional balance, digestion, and nervous system.
Lotus Pose –	Cross-legged yoga sitting posture; heels resting on inner thighs (more advanced than Easy Pose).
Maha Bandh –	"Great Lock," application of neck lock, diaphragm lock, and root lock.
Manipura –	Third chakra, located at the navel point/solar plexus area. Relates to personal initiative, identity, power (or greed) and digestion.
Mantra –	Sound current for elevating mental vibration (ma = mind, tra = vibration). Specific sequence of sounds to stimulate nerve channels to the brain.
Meditation –	Internal experience a person has with his or her inner self; specific yogic techniques combining breath, mantra, mental focus.
Moon Centers –	Eleven centers corresponding to different locations in a womanís body which activate in her body in a unique 28-day cycle.
Mudra –	Yogic hand position.
Mul Bandh –	Root lock, pulling the muscles of the anal sphincter, sex organs, and navel point.
Muladara –	First chakra, located at the base of the spine (anus). Relates to issues of security and survival.
Naad –	Ancient yogic science of sound vibration and its effects.

Panj Shabad –	Five primal sounds (SAA, TAA, NAA, MAA – the AA is the fifth sound).
Pingala –	One of two nerve channels which intertwine around the central spinal nerve. Pingala conducts the male (solar) energy of the body. See Ida.
Prakirti –	Goddess; the feminine divine quality.
Prana –	Life force energy, primarily carried by the breath.
Pranayama –	Yogic breath techniques.
Prayer Mudra –	Yoga hand posture, putting the palms together at the center of the chest, with the fingers pointing up. Creates neutrality of the mind.
Purkha –	Nucleus of God; the male divine quality.
Rock Pose –	Yoga posture, sitting on heels with palms resting on thighs, spine straight and relaxed. Aids digestion.
Sahastara –	Seventh chakra, located at the crown of the head. Relates to a state of divine union or bliss.
Samadhi –	State of perfection or divine bliss.
Shakti –	Feminine God power of the universe.
Shiva –	Masculine God power of the universe.
Shukra Kriya –	Venus Kriyas or couples meditations as taught by Yogi Bhajan.
Shushmana –	Central nerve column of the spine.
Swadhishthama –	Second chakra, located at the sex organs. Relates to creativity and sexuality.

Third Eye –   Ajna or sixth chakra. Seat of intuitive power (pituitary gland). A focus point during meditation.

Uddiyana Bandh –   Diaphragm lock.

Venus Kriyas –   Powerful yogic meditations for couples taught by Yogi Bhajan. Also known as Shukra Kriyas.

Venus Lock –   Yoga hand position; fingers are interlaced (with the left thumb in the web of the right thumb for women and right thumb in the web of the left thumb for men).

Vishudha –   Fifth chakra, located at the throat center. Relates to the thyroid gland and power of projective truth in speech.